WORD WIZARD

Literacy Skills and Activities

Gill Skills

5TH CLASS

Alison Ginnell

g GILL EDUCATION

Contents

How to Use this Book

Comprehension strategies

This book continues building on the comprehension strategies learned at earlier levels of the *Word Wizard* series. Pupils are now exposed to a variety of engaging activities designed to foster their comprehension skills before, during and after reading.

 This symbol indicates a comprehension activity to be carried out **before reading**.

 This symbol indicates a comprehension activity to be carried out **during reading**.

 This symbol indicates a comprehension activity to be carried out **after reading**.

Care has been taken to make these activities as general as possible so that they may be applied to other texts such as a class novel.

Some activities are repeated in order to give pupils sufficient practice in important strategies that will help them to use these strategies independently with future texts.

For a detailed explanation of all comprehension strategies, see page vi.

Vocabulary development

STOP! Use your dictionary to find out the meaning of the **bold** words below.

A stop sign appears before each comprehension reading passage, asking pupils to use their dictionary to find out the meaning of the bold words in the text before reading. This is designed to facilitate the teaching of tricky vocabulary prior to reading the text.

Cloze procedure

A cloze procedure closely linked to the reading passage has been included in each unit. In the first four units (leading up to October mid-term), the missing words are provided in a word box. In subsequent units, the answers can be found on pages 113–114. This allows for much needed practice, helps with confidence-building and develops familiarity with cloze procedures.

Dictation

Three dictation sentences are provided for each unit, incorporating the phonics and grammar taught. Suggestions are provided for extension activities or further revision of grammar.

Assessment

A self-assessment feature appears below each dictation activity.

 I can do this!  I'm getting there.  I need help!

Two units dedicated to revision and assessment are provided at the end of the second and third terms. Each includes a special four-day section designed to prompt meaningful revision of phonics and grammar before assessment begins.

Extra

Each unit concludes with a suggested activity for extension work that facillitates integration within the areas of art, debate, drama and others.

Genre writing approach

The series takes a unique approach to genre writing. At this level, genre writing follows a four-week approach, with a fortnight spent on each unit. Two units are dedicated to each genre.

> Discrete oral language activities act as building blocks for genre writing.

> The second unit dedicated to each genre introduces the **language and grammar** that pupils are expected to include in the genre. They are then asked to **edit and rewrite** the piece of writing drafted in the previous unit.

> The first unit dedicated to each genre explores the **structure** of the genre. Pupils are asked to **plan and draft** a piece of writing, usually linked to the comprehension topic.

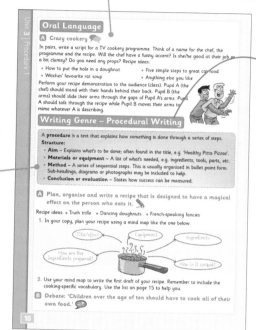

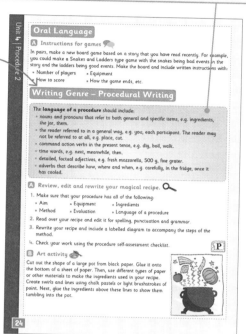

> The reading passage serves as a template for the genre. The teacher can refer to this while outlining the structure of the genre, simply through discussion, or by having pupils highlight or underline the various elements.

> Grammar activities are linked to the genre wherever appropriate.

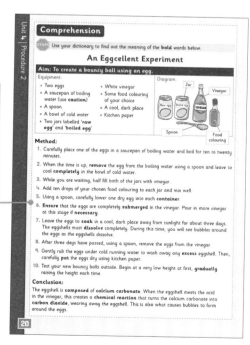

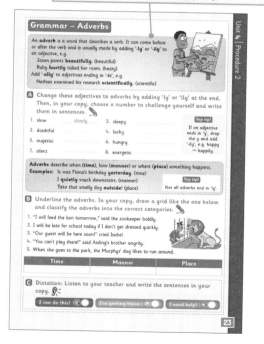

Online resources to support genre writing

- An editable writing frame is provided online to allow pupils to publish their work for an audience.
- A self-assessment checklist is also provided to help pupils edit and self-assess their work.

Comprehension Strategies Guide

Predicting (P) means guessing what will happen. By looking at what has happened in the story already, you can make informed predictions about what might happen next. A book's cover, title, blurb, chapter titles and images also provide clues to help you.

Making Connections (MC) means linking information in the text to something in your own life (text to self), something that you read somewhere else (text to text) or something that you heard about on the television or the radio or from another person (text to world).

Visualising (V) means creating mental pictures based on the text and images.

Questioning (Q): I wonder… This involves asking questions about what you are reading while you read. Keep your mind active and dig deeper into the text.

Word Attack (WA): When you get stuck on a word, use the following bank of Word Attack skills to help you figure it out:

'weather' we, wet, the, her, he, eat, tea, heat	Look for a smaller word in the word.	al-li-ga-tor	Sound out the word. Break it up. Chunk it.
l a ke b oa t d r ea m	Look at the beginning, middle and end of the word.	Prefix Root Suffix	Do you recognise any prefixes, suffixes or root words?
	Look at the images. Is there a clue?	**SKIP IT!**	Skip the word and read the sentence to the end.
	Make a guess. What would make sense?	Context	Use the words around it. Put it in context.
	Go back and re-read.		Use your background knowledge.
	Use your dictionary or thesaurus.		Picture the word in your mind. What do you see?

Determining Importance (DI) means deciding what is relevant or irrelevant. If you were to tell a stranger what the text was about, what would be the key points?

Inferring (I) means reading between the lines.

Clarifying (C) means figuring out a word, a phrase or an idea that you don't understand. Don't give up! Re-read the text or ask for help to understand it more clearly.

Summarising (S) means choosing the key points from the text.

Synthesising (Sy) means using all of your comprehension strategies to understand what you are reading.

Skimming is a **skill** that involves having a quick look through the text to get a general understanding. Headings, images and words that are **bold**, *italicised* or underlined can be useful clues.

Scanning is a **skill** that involves reading quickly through the text to find specific or important information.

Why Do Earthquakes Happen?

Comprehension Strategies

A Before reading: I wonder…

Use the strategy of **Questioning**. Fill in the thought bubbles with questions about the text.

I wonder
How powerful the biggest earthquake was?

I wonder
what is an earthquake?

I wonder
are tsunamis linked with earthquakes?

B Before reading: Dictionary chart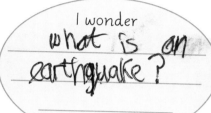

Use the strategy of **Word Attack** and the skill of **Scanning**. Scan the text and write any interesting words in the chart below. Look for clues in the text to try to figure out the meaning. Finally, use a dictionary to find out if you were right.

Word	Meaning from the text	Was I right?
tectonic	tectonic plates make earthquakes	Yes
tsunami	earthquake under the sea	Yes
Ritcher scale	scale to measure earthquakes	Yes
seismologist	measures earthquake	Yes

C During reading: Turn on the lights!

Use the strategy of **Synthesising**. Stop and notice when something in the text is clarified or explained. This is known as a 'lightbulb moment'. Record your lightbulb moments below.

seismologist studies and measures earthquakes.

tectonic plates! rub together and create earthquakes.

D After reading: Important text

Use the strategy of **Determining Importance**. Read back over the text and ring the important words. Explain to your partner why you think these words are important.

Comprehension

 STOP! Use your dictionary to find out the meaning of the **bold** words below.

Why Do Earthquakes Happen?

An earthquake is a sudden shaking or rolling of the earth's **surface**. Most earthquakes are not felt, as they are weak, or they happen deep in the earth's surface or under the sea. Others are so powerful that they can be felt thousands of kilometres away from where they **originated** and cause a lot of **destruction**. Every year, there are millions of earthquakes and over 10,000 people die as a result.

What are tectonic plates?

The earth is made up of four layers. The outer layer is called the crust. This is about 40 km thick and is made up of land, seas and oceans. It is broken into around 20 pieces called tectonic plates. These plates float on the mantle, moving slowly at a rate of about 15 cm a year (the rate at which hair grows). The place where two plates meet is called a fault line. This is where earthquakes **form**.

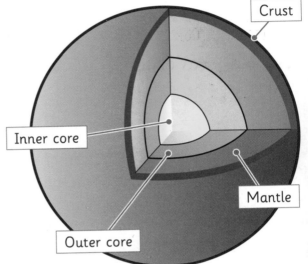

How do tectonic plates cause earthquakes?

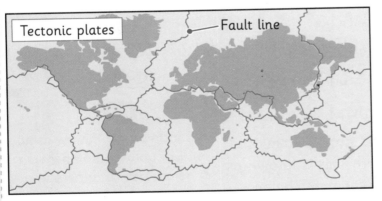

Tectonic plates **constantly** move in different directions. They often crash into, slide under or over, or rub against each other. When plates crash into or **graze** past each other, **tension** is **released** as a great burst of energy. This causes an earthquake. The release of energy is felt as a rumbling or shaking of the crust. The area below ground where this happens is called the hypocentre. The centre of the area above ground where this is felt is called the epicentre. This is where most damage occurs. Earthquakes can cause **landslides**, **tsunamis** and flooding, and often **devastate** entire cities.

How are earthquakes measured?

A seismologist measures the strength of an earthquake on the Richter scale using a seismograph. Unfortunately, seismologists haven't yet figured out how to **predict** when an earthquake will happen. The strongest earthquake ever recorded was in Chile in 1960. It had a magnitude of 9.5.

Luckily for us, Ireland is **relatively** safe from this devastating natural disaster.

A In your copy, go investigate.

1. What is an earthquake?
2. Why can some earthquakes be felt from thousands of kilometres away?
3. Name the four layers of the earth.
4. What causes an earthquake?
5. How do seismologists measure the strength of an earthquake?
6. What other natural disasters can be caused by an earthquake?

B In your copy, give your opinion.

1. Why do you think Ireland is relatively safe from earthquakes?
2. What do you think a seismologist does?
3. Why do you think the earth's outer layer is called the crust?
4. Do you think an earthquake is likely to happen in Japan? Explain.
5. What would you do if an earthquake happened when you were at home?

C Vocabulary: Unscramble and match the words with their meaning.

phmgssaoeri	sotgsliemsoi	qrkuehatae	rcetneipe	ntcioetc tlepsa
seismograph	*seismologist*	*earthquake*	*epicentre*	*tectonic plates*

1. Above-ground centre of an earthquake
2. A scientist who studies earthquakes
3. A rolling or shaking of the earth's surface
4. Sections of the earth's crust
5. An instrument used to measure the strength of an earthquake

D Cloze procedure: 'Earthquake in Haiti'. Fill in the blanks.

2010	an	epicentre	recorded	following	its	poorest	people	Richter

Haiti is _____ island in the Caribbean near Central America. It is the _____ country in the Western Hemisphere and has a history of earthquakes. On January 12th _____, an earthquake whose _____ was near the capital city of Port-au-Prince was recorded with a magnitude of seven on the _____ scale. At least fifty-two aftershocks continued over the _____ twelve days. Major damage was caused in the capital and the surrounding towns and cities. A total of three million _____ were affected, with between 100,000 and 160,000 deaths _____. Countries around the world rushed to Haiti's aid. The country continues in _____ recovery to this day.

Phonics – Homophones

Homophones are words that sound the same, but are spelled differently and have different meanings.

Examples: sail – to sail a boat

sale – when goods are sold at a cheaper price than usual

A Cross out the incorrect homophones.

1. **Their/They're** playing in the camogie final this evening.

2. "Come over **here/hear** and help me look for my book," pleaded Sam.

3. I have **too/two** brothers. **There/Their** names are Stephen and Brendan.

4. "Keep it down. **You're/Your too/to** loud!" called Ms Daly **two/to** her class.

5. The dog buried **it's/its** bone over **there/they're**.

6. Did you **hear/here** Ed Sheeran's new song? **Its/it's** brilliant!

7. **They're/Their** going **to/two** learn **too/to** play the violin.

B Complete the crossword using the correct homophones. Use your dictionary to help you.

Across

3. Part of a whole (peace/piece)

5. To speak with a normal to high volume (allowed/aloud)

6. The part of the body between the ribs and the hips (waist/waste)

7. Not strong (week/weak)

8. To involve oneself without being asked (meddle/medal)

Down

1. Pulled tight (taut/taught)

2. Birds commonly found on farms; chickens, ducks, etc. (fowl/foul)

3. The feet of an animal (pause/paws)

4. Harsh or rough (course/coarse)

7. The measure of heaviness of an object (weight/wait)

C In your copy, write sentences with the unused words above. Pick a number to challenge yourself.

Grammar – Capital Letters and Punctuation

We use a capital letter for:
- the start of a sentence.
- the pronoun 'I'.
- the names of people and places.
- the main words in the titles of books, films, TV programmes, etc.
- the days of the week, months and festivals (but not the seasons).

Top tip!

We also use single speech marks to show the titles of books, films, TV programmes, etc.

A Ring the words that should have a capital letter.

1. i am going on a trip during the hallowe'en holidays. i will visit london and paris.
2. on friday, i went to see 'despicable me' in the cinema with peter and paul.
3. in december, hannah celebrates christmas, while joseph celebrates hanukkah.
4. my parents gave me 'mr stink' by david walliams for my birthday on monday.
5. there are three months in summer: may, june and july.
6. callum's favourite TV programme is called 'adventure time'.
7. next winter, i will visit my aunt and cousins in cork.

A sentence begins with a capital letter and ends with:
- a full stop, e.g. My name is Jane.
- a question mark, e.g. What is your favourite colour?
- an exclamation mark, e.g. Ouch!

Ouch!

B Ring the words that should have a capital letter and insert the correct punctuation.

1. is easter in march or april this year
2. oh no, my new jeans are ripped
3. my favourite book is 'diary of a wimpy kid'
4. my trip to romania was amazing
5. when will we arrive at croke park
6. i will visit dublin in march to see the st patrick's day parade
7. should i visit new york or washington when i am in america this spring

C Dictation: Listen to your teacher and write the sentences in your copy.

I can do this!   I'm getting there.   I need help!

Oral Language

A Use the pictures to help you explain the life-cycle of a frog.

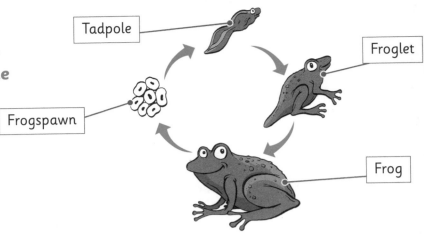

Tadpole

Froglet

Frogspawn

Frog

Writing Genre – Explanation Writing

An **explanation** is a text that explains how something works, or how or why something happens.

Structure:

- **Title** – Usually presented in the form of a question.
- **Definition** – A short description or fact about the thing that you will be explaining.
- **Description** – A logical, step-by-step explanation of how or reasons why. This is often supported by diagrams.
- **Summary** – A brief summary of the main points.

Top tip!

Explanations are not 'how to' texts. Those are instructions.

A Plan and write an explanation of how something happens.

Use what you know from science or geography, such as:

- The water cycle
- The seasons
- The life-cycle of an animal, an insect or a plant
- Earthquakes
- Breathing
- Anything else that you have learned about

1. Plan your explanation in your copy using a mind map like the one below.

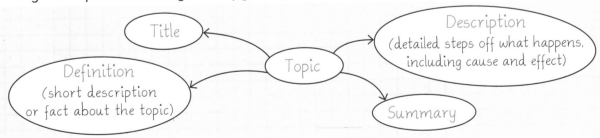

Title

Definition
(short description
or fact about the topic)

Topic

Description
(detailed steps off what happens,
including cause and effect)

Summary

2. Use your mind map to write the first draft of your explanation.

B Drama

Read back over the cloze procedure on page 3. Imagine that your class is a group of disaster experts called in from all over the world to help Haiti recover from its disaster. Decide on who your character is, what your special skills are and what your expert plan for helping Haiti is. Walk around the room introducing yourself and explaining your action plan.

The Life-cycle of the Salamander

Comprehension Strategies

A Before reading: Add text.

Use the strategy of **Predicting**. Cover the text and look only at the image. In pairs, discuss what text might accompany the image.

B Before reading: KWL chart

Use the strategies of **Making Connections** and **Questioning**. Use the chart below to record your background knowledge (schema) on the salamander and anything that you hope to find out from reading the text. Record what you have learned after reading.

KWL Chart		
What I know	**What I want to know**	**What I have learned**
A Salamander is a type of amphibian.	What does a Salamander eat? What is a Salamanders habitat? Is there many Salamanders is there left?	

C During reading: Fabulous five

Use the strategy of **Determining Importance**. While reading, record five key words in the text. Then, in groups, compare your 'fabulous five' and justify why you thought these were the most important words in the text.

Larvae   eggs   gills   metamorphis   amphibian

D After reading: Oral summary

Use the strategy of **Summarising**. In pairs, summarise the main points of the text. Present your summary orally to the class.

Comprehension

 STOP! Use your dictionary to find out the meaning of the **bold** words below.

The Life-cycle of the Salamander

The salamander is a fascinating **amphibian** that has been in existence since the time of the dinosaurs. There are over 500 different **species** of salamander, with **variations** in colour, pattern and size. However, they all go through the same changes when growing into adulthood.

Eggs

All female salamanders lay their eggs underwater. The eggs are covered in a protective layer of jelly. This also helps them **fasten** to plants and twigs. Some species of salamander live underwater and care for their eggs before they hatch. However, others live on land, so after laying the eggs, they leave them to grow and hatch by themselves.

Larvae

The eggs take about four weeks to hatch. The salamanders that **emerge** are called larvae. Like tadpoles, they have a long tail and no legs, and they use **gills** to breathe underwater. Once hatched, the larvae have to **fend** for themselves. They are strong enough to hunt for food under water.

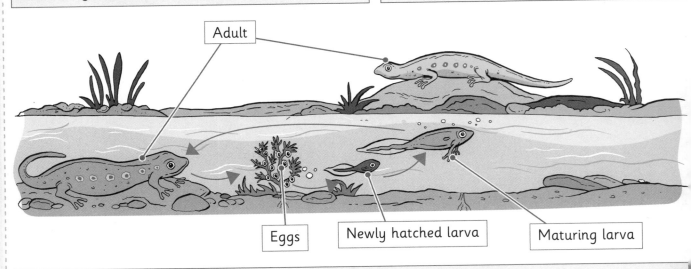

Adult

Eggs

Newly hatched larva

Maturing larva

Adulthood

In order to become adults, the larvae undergo a **metamorphosis** that begins at about three weeks old. They grow front legs first, followed by back legs. Finally, their thin tail grows thicker. Some species keep their gills and remain living under water. However, most grow lungs in place of gills and live on land. The final **phase** of the metamorphosis is complete when they develop their adult colouring. Adult salamanders mate and lay eggs in the place where they hatched. For some, this is easy, because they **remained** close to their birthplace. Others must use their strong sense of smell to locate their birthplace.

Salamanders are amazing animals that undergo **drastic** changes in their appearance to reach adulthood. This is **despite** the fact that they haven't changed their characteristics since they shared the earth with the dinosaurs.

A In your copy, go investigate.

1. How many different types of salamander are there?
2. What are the three main stages in the life-cycle of the salamander?
3. Why do larvae need gills?
4. How old are larvae when they begin to change?
5. Where do all salamanders lay their eggs?
6. Name two differences between salamanders that live in water and on land.

B In your copy, give your opinion.

1. How do you think the jelly helps to protect the eggs?
2. Why do you think salamanders return to where they were born to lay their eggs?
3. Why do you think the tiger salamander is so named?
4. Would you like a salamander as a pet? Explain.
5. What type of care do you think a pet salamander would need?
6. In your copy, design and name a new species of salamander.

C Vocabulary: Match these cause-and-effect sentences.

(Hint: Cause and effect is when one event causes another to happen.)

1. Salamander eggs are covered in jelly. ▪	▪ They have gills to breathe.
2. A salamander larva is three weeks old. ▪	▪ The eggs stick to the twigs.
3. Some salamanders live underwater. ▪	▪ They grow lungs to breathe.
4. Some salamanders live on land. ▪	▪ They can find their way home easily.
5. Salamanders have a strong sense of smell. ▪	▪ It begins metamorphosis.

D Cloze procedure: 'More About Salamanders'. Fill in the blanks.

grow	patterns	fire	gills	salamander	predators	long	breathe

There are many different species of _____.
The largest, the Chinese giant, can _____ up to 2 m
long. The smallest is about 1.7 cm _____. All
salamanders need to _____ to get oxygen.
Some get oxygen under water using their _____

Chinese giant salamander

and others have lungs. Salamanders come in different colours and _____.
The brightly coloured species are often poisonous. Their bright colours warn
_____ to stay away from them. The _____ salamander sprays a
poison from its back that burns the eyes and mouth of its victim.

Phonics – Suffixes

A **suffix** is a letter or group of letters added to the end of a root word to change its meaning.

- If the root word ends in two consonants, add the suffix, e.g. walk → walk**ed**.
- If the root word has a short vowel and one consonant, double the last consonant and add the suffix, e.g. fun → fun**ny**.
- If the root word ends in 'e' and the suffix begins with a vowel, drop the 'e' and add the suffix, e.g. come → com**ing**.
- If the root word ends with a consonant and a 'y', change the 'y' to 'i' and add the suffix, e.g. friendly → friend**liness**, but enjoy → enjoy**able**.
- If the suffix begins with a consonant, add the suffix, e.g. wonder**ful**.

A Ring the correct spelling of each word.

1. quickken / quicken
2. beautyful / beautiful
3. runing / running
4. biggest / bigest
5. smileing / smiling
6. laziness / lazyness
7. bikeing / biking
8. doubtful / doubtfful
9. internship / internnship

B Use a suffix to change each word in brackets.

-ment	-ly	-ful	-able	-ous	-est
-er	-ing	-ed	-ship	-en	

1. The new girl in my art class is really (friend)   .
2. Pam gets paid a (consider)   amount more than Jim.
3. Our class got great (enjoy)   from our school tour.
4. Our teacher was (fury)   when Jack broke the window.
5. The (court)   of the prince and the princess was short.
6. Meredith is the (fast)   (swim)   in our club.
7. My dad (bake)   me a (beauty)   birthday cake.
8. Michael spent his weekend (piece)   together a jigsaw puzzle.
9. I could hear the music (quick)   towards the end of the song.

C Make a new word using each of these suffixes. Choose a number to challenge yourself and write some sentences in your copy.

1. ment	2. ly	3. ful	4. able
5. ness	6. est	7. er	8. ing
9. ed	10. ship	11. en	12. ous

Grammar – Nouns

Nouns are naming words. They refer to people, places, things and animals, e.g. girl, school, cup and dog. These are examples of **common nouns**. Common nouns do not need a capital letter.

Proper nouns refer to the **name** of a person, a place or an occasion. Proper nouns always need a capital letter, e.g. John, Dubai, March, Hallowe'en.

A Underline the common nouns and ring the proper nouns.

1. Pandas are mostly found in China.
2. For my birthday in July, I would like to get a bicycle from my parents.
3. On St Patrick's Day, I like to watch the parade with my family.
4. My cousins live in a bungalow in Navan, which is a town in Meath.
5. On Sunday, Hannah and Penny went to the shop and bought some books.

We can classify **nouns** by their **gender**.
- **Feminine**: female nouns, e.g. girl, aunt
- **Masculine**: male nouns, e.g. bull, father
- **Common**: nouns that can be either feminine or masculine, e.g. cousin
- **Neuter**: nouns that are neither feminine nor masculine, e.g. pen

B In your copy, draw a grid like the one below and organise the nouns into the correct categories.

book   sibling   chair   boy   teacher   car   mother   nurse   sister   nephew
rooster   tree   man   mouse   wife   microwave   queen   student   prince   doe

Feminine	Masculine	Common	Neuter

C In your copy, change each underlined noun to the opposite gender.

1. The <u>king</u> and <u>queen</u> were proud of their new <u>daughter</u>, the <u>princess</u>.
2. My <u>mother</u> took my <u>brother</u> shopping to buy <u>him</u> some new clothes.
3. The <u>lion</u> cared for <u>his</u> new cubs when they were born.
4. The <u>lord</u> will inherit <u>his</u> fortune when <u>his</u> <u>uncle</u> passes away.

> **Top tip!**
>
> Pronouns must always agree with the gender of nouns in a sentence.

D Dictation: Listen to your teacher and write the sentences in your copy.

 I can do this!   I'm getting there.   I need help!

Oral Language

A Cause and effect

Cause and effect is when one event causes another to happen. In pairs, take turns giving an example of a cause (an event). Your partner must explain the possible effects.

Cause		Effect
Freda goes to every camogie training session. She has been working hard all year.		<ul><li>Freda improves her camogie skills.</li><li>Freda scores a goal in her camogie match.</li><li>Freda wins player of the match.</li></ul>
Arminas and Toby throw a ball inside the house.		<ul><li>They break a window.</li><li>(You decide.)</li><li>(You decide.)</li></ul>

Writing Genre – Explanation Writing

The **language of an explanation** should include:

- general, non-human subjects, e.g. the thermometer, the butterfly, bicycles.
- time conjunctions, e.g. first, then, following.
- cause-and-effect conjunctions, e.g. because, if/then, so, this results in.
- action verbs, e.g. changes, flies, expands.
- timeless present tense verbs, e.g. turns, flows.
- clear and factual adjectives, e.g. atmospheric, fully-grown.

A Review, edit and rewrite your explanation.

1. Make sure that your explanation has all of the following:
   - Title
   - Definition
   - Description
   - Summary
   - Explanation language

2. Read over your explanation and edit it for spelling, punctuation and grammar.

3. Rewrite your explanation and include a labelled diagram to accompany each step of the sequence.

4. Check your work using the explanation self-assessment checklist.

P

B Drama

In pairs, pick one of the cause-and-effect scenarios that you discussed in the oral language activity above. Create a three-step freeze-frame tableau and have the rest of the class fill in a cause-and-effect chart, similar to the one above, on the board.

Healthy Pitta Pizzas

3

Comprehension Strategies

A Before reading: At a glance

Use the strategy of **Questioning** and the skill of **Skimming** and take half a minute to skim through the text to get a general idea of what it is about. Pay close attention to image, headings and bold words. Then, work in pairs and ask each other questions. Check how many you got right after you have read the text fully.

B During reading: Five senses

Use the strategy of **Visualising**. Stop reading and think about what you can see, hear, smell, taste and touch.

C After reading: Fact or fib?

Use the strategy of **Synthesising**. Write three facts and one fib about the text. Then, in pairs, swap your lists and find each other's fib.

Facts

1. _____

   _____

2. _____

   _____

3. _____

   _____

4. _____

   _____

Comprehension

 STOP! Use your dictionary to find out the meaning of the **bold** words below.

Healthy Pitta Pizzas

Aim: To learn how to make healthy pitta pizzas.

Makes: **4**	Preparation time: 10 minutes	Cooking time: 10–15 minutes

Ingredients:

- Four wholewheat pitta breads
- One tin of chopped tomatoes (for sauce)
- 50 g fresh mozzarella (pre-grated is fine too)
- Half a red onion
- One yellow pepper
- One large tomato
- Fresh basil

Equipment:

- A grill
- A chopping board
- A knife
- A cheese grater

Diagram:

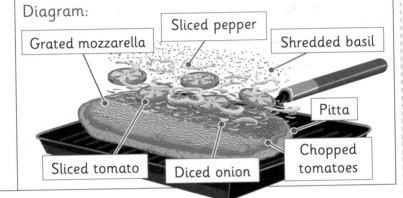

Grated mozzarella · Sliced pepper · Shredded basil · Pitta · Chopped tomatoes · Diced onion · Sliced tomato

Experiment!

Try adding your favourite vegetables, such as courgette or mushrooms. You could even add ham or pepperoni as a treat.

Method:

1. **Preheat** the grill at the medium setting. **Meanwhile**, lightly toast the pittas in the toaster.
2. Grate the mozzarella (if needed).
3. **Dice** the red onion and thinly slice the tomato.
4. Remove the seeds from the pepper and thinly slice.
5. **Finely shred** the basil.

To assemble:

1. Spoon the chopped tomatoes onto the pitta bread.
2. Sprinkle the grated cheese over the chopped tomatoes. **Scatter** the diced onion.
3. Divide the tomato and pepper slices evenly between the four pitta breads and lay them over the onion. Scatter the basil over the vegetables.
4. **Place** the pittas under the grill and leave until the cheese has begun to melt. Be sure to keep an eye on them while they cook.
5. Use oven mitts to remove the tray from the grill.
6. Serve to family and friends with a salad or coleslaw, and enjoy.

Wow your family and friends by **arranging** the toppings as a face. Use the tomato slices for eyes, the pepper for a mouth and a **sprig** of basil for a nose.

A In your copy, go investigate.

1. What equipment is needed to make this recipe?
2. How long do the pizzas take to make altogether?
3. What does the author suggest adding to the pizzas?
4. How should you prepare the red onion?
5. What is mozzarella? Find at least one sentence in the text that might tell you.
6. What about this recipe makes it healthy?

B In your copy, give your opinion.

1. Would you need an adult's help for any part of this recipe? Why/Why not?
2. What might happen if you do not check on the pizzas while they cook?
3. Why should you use the oven mitts to remove the tray from under the grill?
4. Would you like to make this recipe? Why/Why not?
5. If you were to make this recipe, what toppings would you add?
6. What other food could you arrange into interesting shapes?

C Vocabulary

Make a list of all of the food-preparation and cooking language in the text. Add to it with your own words. You might like to research some recipes to help you.

knead			

D Cloze procedure: 'Kitchen Catastrophe'. Fill in the blanks.

favourites   kitchen   blaring   in   full   burned   starving   himself   watch   later

Luke was home alone and he was _____. He couldn't wait for his mum or dad to get home, so he decided to make _____ a toasted sandwich. He added all of his _____: ham, cheese, tomato and onion. He shoved the tray under the grill and decided to _____ the match while he waited. What felt like seconds _____, he was awoken by his dad yelling from the _____. Oops, he'd fallen asleep! The whole house was _____ of smoke and the smoke alarm was _____. Luckily, his dad had got home just _____ time. There was no saving the sandwich though; it had been _____ to a crisp.

Phonics – '-age', '-ege'

A **syllable** is a part of a word that usually has one vowel sound.
Example: The word '**computer**' has three syllables – **com/pu/ter**.
The syllables '**-age**' and '**-ege**' both make an /**ij**/ sound when the first syllable of the word is stressed (said slightly louder to give it more emphasis).
Examples: coll**ege**   man**age**
Most words with the /**ij**/ sound are spelled with '**-age**'. The four most common '**-ege**' words are included in section A below. Look out for them!

A **Split the words below into their syllables. (Clapping out the word as you say it can help with this.) Ring the stressed syllable.**

1. encourage (en)/cour/age

2. college _____

3. hostage _____

4. orphanage _____

5. allege _____

6. heritage _____

7. manage _____

8. sacrilege _____

9. spillage _____

10. privilege _____

11. sewage _____

12. disadvantage _____

Challenge: Which word above has a stress on the last syllable?

B **Write one sentence using all four '-ege' words above.**

_____

C **Complete the words below using '-age' or '-ege'.**

1. Dad was very angry when the airline charged extra for our bagg_____ .

2. "It is a privil_____ to meet you," said Konur when he met the president.

3. Beans, mashed potatoes and saus_____s are my favourite foods.

4. Shane showed great cour_____ when he stood up to the bullies.

5. Jasmine would like to study medicine in coll_____.

6. Polish is Julia's first langu_____ and English is her second.

7. In Islam, it is a sacril_____ to draw a picture of the prophet Mohammed.

8. "Naoise, can you bring this mess_____ to Mr Hill, please?" asked Ms Smith.

9. The lawyer all_____d that the witness was lying to protect his friend.

10. It is a great advant_____ to be tall when competing in the high jump.

Grammar – Verbs

A **verb** is a doing or an action word.
Examples: I **live** in Ireland.   Maria **scrubbed** the floor.
We can use interesting verbs to make our sentences more exciting.
Example: The boy **ran** home. → The boy **sprinted** home.

A Underline the verb/s. Then, rewrite each sentence in your copy, but change at least one verb to a more interesting one. ✏️

1. The rat ate the cheese that it had found on the floor.
2. "Stop looking out the window," said the teacher.
3. Nikita walked around his bedroom on his broken leg.
4. The expensive vase was broken when it hit the floor.
5. I smiled when I saw the horse running around the field.

Top tip!

Use a thesaurus to help you!

Some **verbs** need one or more 'helping' verbs in order to make sense.
Example: I **was** **walking** to the shop.

B Ring the verbs and underline the 'helping' verbs. ✏️

1. Mateusz is helping his mum with the washing-up.
2. We are going to Causey Farm on our school tour this year.
3. The thief was sneaking around the house so he would not be heard.
4. "I would like strawberries on my birthday cake please," answered Sofia.
5. "Zaina, you should visit your granny after school today," called her mother.

C Use the correct 'helping' verbs to complete the sentences.

will	to	can	has	might	to	does	are

1. Tia   clean her room when she gets home from football training.
2. "I   sing a few lines of the Hallowe'en song now," said Dylan proudly.
3. My mum told me that we   get a dog if we promise   take care of it.
4. It is easy   lose your balance if you are not looking where you   going.
5. Kai   been telling his friends for years that he   not like spinach.

D Dictation: Listen to your teacher and write the sentences in your copy. 👂

(I can do this! 👍 ⚪)   (I'm getting there. ✋ ⚪)   (I need help! 👎 ⚪)

17

Oral Language

A Crazy cookery

In pairs, write a script for a TV cookery programme. Think of a name for the chef, the programme and the recipe. Will the chef have a funny accent? Is she/he good at their job or a bit clumsy? Do you need any props? Recipe ideas:

- How to put the hole in a doughnut
- Witches' favourite rat soup
- Five simple steps to great cat food
- Anything else you like

Perform your recipe demonstration to the audience (class). Pupil A (the chef) should stand with their hands behind their back. Pupil B (the arms) should slide their arms through the gaps of Pupil A's arms. Pupil A should talk through the recipe while Pupil B moves their arms to mime whatever A is describing.

Writing Genre – Procedural Writing

A **procedure** is a text that explains how something is done through a series of steps.

Structure:

- **Aim** – Explains what's to be done; often found in the title, e.g. 'Healthy Pitta Pizzas'.
- **Materials or equipment** – A list of what's needed, e.g. ingredients, tools, parts, etc.
- **Method** – A series of sequential steps. This is usually organised in bullet point form. Sub-headings, diagrams or photographs may be included to help.
- **Conclusion or evaluation** – States how success can be measured.

A Plan, organise and write a recipe that is designed to have a magical effect on the person who eats it.

Recipe ideas: ■ Truth trifle ■ Dancing doughnuts ■ French-speaking fancies

1. In your copy, plan your recipe using a mind map like the one below.

2. Use your mind map to write the first draft of your recipe. Remember to include the cooking-specific vocabulary. Use the list on page 15 to help you.

B Debate: 'Children over the age of ten should have to cook all of their own food.'

An Eggcellent Experiment

Comprehension Strategies

A Before reading: Figure it out!

Use the strategy of **Inferring**. Use the title, aim, equipment and diagram to figure out what the method of this science experiment will be. In pairs, decide on at least five steps.

They will put the eggs in food colouring and vinegar and the eggs will go hard. Then he might test them

B During reading: This reminds me of...

Use the strategy of **Making Connections**. While reading, stop along the way to make connections to:

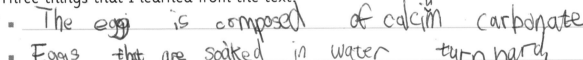

- yourself – This reminds me of a time I ...
- another text – This reminds me of something I read...
- the outside world – This reminds me of what I know about ...

This reminds me of...

C After reading: 3, 2, 1

Use the strategy of **Synthesising**.

Three things that I learned from the text:

- The egg is composed of calcium carbonate
- Eggs that are soaked in water turn hard
-

Two interesting facts in the text:

-
-
-

One question that I still have:

-

Comprehension

STOP! Use your dictionary to find out the meaning of the **bold** words below.

An Eggcellent Experiment

Aim: To create a bouncy ball using an egg.

Equipment:

- Two eggs
- A saucepan of boiling water (use **caution**)
- A spoon
- A bowl of cold water
- Two jars labelled '**raw egg**' and '**boiled egg**'

- White vinegar
- Some food colouring of your choice
- A cool, dark place
- Kitchen paper

Diagram:

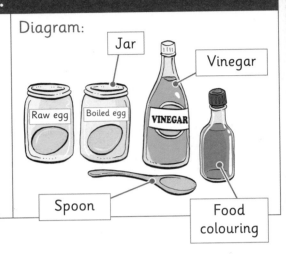

Method:

1. Carefully place one of the eggs in a saucepan of boiling water and boil for ten to twenty minutes.

2. When the time is up, **remove** the egg from the boiling water using a spoon and leave to cool **completely** in the bowl of cold water.

3. While you are waiting, half fill both of the jars with vinegar.

4. Add ten drops of your chosen food colouring to each jar and mix well.

5. Using a spoon, carefully lower one dry egg into each **container**.

6. **Ensure** that the eggs are completely **submerged** in the vinegar. Pour in more vinegar at this stage if **necessary**.

7. Leave the eggs to **soak** in a cool, dark place away from sunlight for about three days. The eggshells must **dissolve** completely. During this time, you will see bubbles around the eggs as the eggshells dissolve.

8. After three days have passed, using a spoon, remove the eggs from the vinegar.

9. Gently rub the eggs under cold running water to wash away any **excess** eggshell. Then, carefully **pat** the eggs dry using kitchen paper.

10. Test your new bouncy balls outside. Begin at a very low height at first, **gradually** raising the height each time.

Conclusion:

The eggshell is **composed** of **calcium carbonate**. When the eggshell meets the acid in the vinegar, this creates a **chemical reaction** that turns the calcium carbonate into **carbon dioxide**, wearing away the eggshell. This is also what causes bubbles to form around the eggs.

A In your copy, go investigate.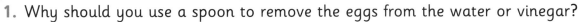

1. What equipment do you need to carry out this experiment?

2. In step 6, why should you add more vinegar to the jar?

3. For how long should you leave the eggs in the vinegar?

4. Where should you store the jars while waiting for the eggshells to dissolve?

5. What is an eggshell made of?

6. Why do bubbles form around the eggs?

B In your copy, give your opinion.

1. Why should you use a spoon to remove the eggs from the water or vinegar?

2. Explain why you should only half fill the jars with vinegar at first.

3. Why do you think you should test the bouncy eggs outside?

4. Which egg do you think would make the best bouncy ball? Explain.

5. Do you think you should eat these eggs after the experiment? Why/Why not?

6. Would you like to try this experiment? Why/Why not?

C Vocabulary: Unscramble and match the words with their meaning.

nabocr idxodie	pceodsmo	oiesldsv	hlcmaiec tneocria	dgubesrem

1. Made up of

2. A process in which a new substance is created

3. To make a solution by mixing completely with a liquid

4. A colourless, odourless gas found in the atmosphere

5. Completely covered

D Cloze procedure: 'Science Fair Disaster'. Fill in the blanks.

confident	her	volcanic	had	forward	Monday	hard	Behold	sighed	room

It was _____ morning, the day of the 5th Class Science Fair. Keith had been looking _____ to presenting his project all year. As the judges walked around the _____ , they complimented Suzy's _____ eruption and Nathan's static electricity experiment. Keith was nervous, but _____ that he would impress them with the bouncy balls he _____ made by soaking eggs in vinegar. "_____ my Eggcellent Experiment!" he announced, bouncing the egg _____ on the table. SPLAT! The egg exploded all over the judges. "Maybe you'll win the prize next year," Keith's teacher _____ as she wiped egg from _____ glasses.

Phonics – '-able', '-ible'

-**ible** and -**able** are suffixes added to words to make them into adjectives.

-**able** is used when the root is a word by itself, e.g. comfort**able**.

For words ending in '**e**' remove the '**e**', unless they end in '**ce**' or '**ge**'.

Examples: adore → ador**able**   change → change**able**

-**ible** is usually used when the root is not a word by itself, e.g. leg**ible**.

A Tick the correct spelling of the '-able' and '-ible' words below.

sensable	recyclible	huggable	flexible	inflatable
sensible	recyclable	huggible	flexable	inflatilbe

convertable	stackable	inedible	invisable	refillable
convertible	stackible	inedable	invisible	refillible

B Complete the crossword using '-able' and '-ible' words.

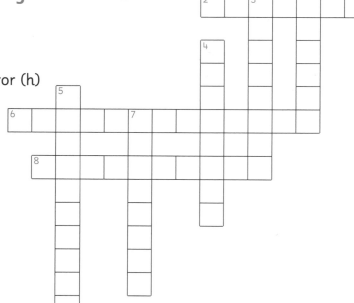

Across

2. Extremely unpleasant, causing horror (h)

6. Lack of responsibility (i)

8. Items that you can afford (a)

Down

1. Can be seen (v)

3. Can be trusted or relied upon (r)

4. Can be done (p)

5. Makes a profit (p)

7. Easily transported (p)

C In your copy, write some of the '-able' and '-ible' words above in sentences. Choose a number to challenge yourself.

Grammar – Adverbs

An **adverb** is a word that describes a verb. It can come before or after the verb and is usually made by adding '**-ly**' or '**-ily**' to an adjective, e.g.

Jason paints **beautifully**. (beautiful)

Ruby **hastily** tidied her room. (hasty)

Add '**-ally**' to adjectives ending in '**-ic**', e.g.

Nathan examined his research **scientifically**. (scientific)

A Change these adjectives to adverbs by adding 'ly' or 'ily' at the end. Then, in your copy, choose a number to challenge yourself and write them in sentences.

1. slow _____slowly_____
2. sleepy _____
3. doubtful _____
4. lucky _____
5. majestic _____
6. hungry _____
7. silent _____
8. energetic _____

Top tip!

If an adjective ends in 'y', drop the y and add '-ily', e.g. happy → happily.

Adverbs describe when (**time**), how (**manner**) or where (**place**) something happens.

Examples: It was Fiona's birthday **yesterday**. (time)

I **quietly** snuck downstairs. (manner)

Take that smelly dog **outside**! (place)

Top tip!

Not all adverbs end in 'ly'.

B Underline the adverbs. In your copy, draw a grid like the one below and classify the adverbs into the correct categories.

1. "I will feed the lion tomorrow," said the zookeeper boldly.
2. I will be late for school today if I don't get dressed quickly.
3. "Our guest will be here soon!" cried Isobel.
4. "You can't play there!" said Aisling's brother angrily.
5. When she goes to the park, the Murphys' dog likes to run around.

Time	Manner	Place

C Dictation: Listen to your teacher and write the sentences in your copy.

 I can do this!   I'm getting there.   I need help!

23

Oral Language

A Instructions for games

In pairs, make a new board game based on a story that you have read recently. For example you could make a Snakes and Ladders type game with the snakes being bad events in the story and the ladders being good events. Make the board and include written instructions with.

- Number of players
- Equipment
- How to score
- How the game ends, etc.

Writing Genre – Procedural Writing

The **language of a procedure** should include:

- nouns and pronouns that refer to both general and specific items, e.g. ingredients, the jar, them.
- the reader referred to in a general way, e.g. you, each participant. The reader may not be referred to at all, e.g. place, cut.
- command action verbs in the present tense, e.g. dig, boil, walk.
- time words, e.g. next, meanwhile, then.
- detailed, factual adjectives, e.g. fresh mozzarella, 500 g, fine grater.
- adverbs that describe how, where and when, e.g. carefully, in the fridge, once it has cooled.

A Review, edit and rewrite your magical recipe.

1. Make sure that your procedure has all of the following:

   - Aim
   - Equipment
   - Ingredients
   - Method
   - Evaluation
   - Language of a procedure

2. Read over your recipe and edit it for spelling, punctuation and grammar.

3. Rewrite your recipe and include a labelled diagram to accompany the steps of the method.

4. Check your work using the procedure self-assessment checklist.

P

B Art activity

Cut out the shape of a large pot from black paper. Glue it onto the bottom of a sheet of paper. Then, use different types of paper or other materials to make the ingredients used in your recipe. Create swirls and lines using chalk pastels or light brushstrokes of paint. Next, glue the ingredients above these lines to show them tumbling into the pot.

The Big, Bad Wolf's Complaint

Comprehension Strategies

A Before reading: Crystal ball

Use the strategy of **Predicting**. Look at the title and image and use your crystal ball to predict what will happen in the text.

I predict that…

I imagine that…

I wonder if…

I think that…

I think that … will happen, because…

Maybe… will happen, because…

B During reading: Changing images

Use the strategy of **Visualising**. Draw an image to show what you can picture…

Before reading	During reading	After reading
you're ruining my flowers	aaaa chooo	

C After reading: What's the story?

Use the strategy of **Determining Importance**. Record key words from the text that show …

The setting	The characters	The main events
The wolfs neighbourhood	Ham, pork and bacon pig. The big bad wolf.	The wolf blew the houses down. He sat in hot water.

D After reading: Report card

Use the strategy of **Inferring**. Think about what you have learned about the Big, Bad Wolf and complete his school report card.

Subject	Grade	Comment
Cooking		
Making friends		
Communicating		
Climbing and balance		

Comprehension

STOP! Use your dictionary to find out the meaning of the **bold** words below.

The Big, Bad Wolf's Complaint

New Message

To onceuponatimelawyers@FTCmail.com

From huffpuff@FTCmail.com   Cc Bcc

Subject Unprovoked attack

Dear Mr A. Tourney,

I write to you with regard to your **clients**, **Messrs** Pork, Bacon and Ham Pigg, on whose property I **sustained** a terrible injury in May of last year.

I refer to the **incident** in which I attempted to welcome the three brothers to the neighbourhood, only to be met with increased **hostility** on each occasion. The first brother, a famously poor builder, had the nerve to blame me when his **ramshackle** new home fell down around him. If a mere yawn could **disassemble** his property, I hardly think that I should be to blame. Who builds a house out of straw anyway?

The second of the three was even worse. He and his brother **barred** the doors and windows and stood on the other side shouting some nonsense about their hairy chins. I'm sure I don't need to tell you, Sir, that I don't care to hear of the personal grooming problems of my new neighbours. Can I really be to blame if this house also came crashing down? All I did was sneeze!

This brings me to my main **grievance**. At this point, the welcome cookies I had baked were getting cold and I was **exhausted** from chasing my **plump** neighbours around the countryside. I admit that I climbed onto the roof, but only in order to properly communicate to my new friends that I had no **intention** of eating them. Well, the third brother wasn't much of a builder either, because I slipped on one of his poorly-secured tiles and **plunged** forward into the chimney. What awaited me there was cruelty beyond imagining. The Piggs had lit a fire! Now, I know the brothers say that this was only to cook their **supper**, but this is a lie. Those evil brothers intended to boil me alive. Luckily, I have quick **reflexes** and was able to hop straight out of the steaming cauldron, but not before I **scalded** my poor tail raw. I can still hear their squeals of delight as I dashed out of there.

Having presented my case to you in a clear manner, I am sure there can be no doubt that I have been wronged. I expect a written apology from the Pigg brothers and **compensation** of no less than two **offspring** from each **offending** party.

Kind regards,

Mr B. B. Wolf

A In your copy, go investigate. 🔍

1. In what month did the wolf try to visit the Piggs?
2. According to the wolf, what caused the second house to fall down?
3. What gift had the wolf made for the Piggs?
4. How did the wolf attempt to talk to the brothers at the third house?
5. How did the wolf fall into the chimney?
6. What injury did the wolf sustain?

B In your copy, give your opinion. 💭

1. What do you think the letters 'FTC' might stand for in the e-mail addresses?
2. Do you think the Piggs are good builders? Why/Why not?
3. When do you think the wolf baked the cookies for the Piggs? Explain.
4. Why does the wolf ask for 'two offspring from each offending party' as compensation?
5. What would you have done if you were the Piggs?
6. Do you think the lawyer will believe the wolf? Why/Why not?

C Vocabulary ✏️

1. Match each abbreviation (shortened word) to the full word.

   (a) Mr ▪   ▪ councillor
   (b) Dr ▪   ▪ misters
   (c) Cllr ▪   ▪ road
   (d) Messrs ▪   ▪ street
   (e) Rd ▪   ▪ mister
   (f) St ▪   ▪ doctor

   Top tip!
   An abbreviation using the last letter of the word does not need a full stop, e.g. Mr – Mister.
   Other abbreviations do, e.g. Aug. – August.

2. Write the full word for these common abbreviations.

   (a) phone _____
   (b) fridge _____
   (c) plane _____
   (d) hippo _____
   (e) bike _____
   (f) TV _____

D Cloze procedure: 'The Three Little Pigs'. Fill in the blanks. ✏️

Once upon a _time_, there lived _three_ little pigs. They decided to move out of home and build _their_ own houses. The first little pig built his house with straw. The second pig built his house with sticks. The third pig built his house with _bricks_. One day, the big, bad _wolf_ came along. He blew down _the_ house made with straw and he blew down the house made with sticks. He could not _blow_ down the house made with bricks, so he climbed _onto_ the roof. The three little pigs lit a _fire_ and the wolf fell into it. He _ran_ away and the pigs lived happily ever after.

Phonics – Negative Prefixes

A prefix is a part of a word that is added to the beginning of the word.

A negative prefix changes the word to its opposite meaning.

Example: believable → **un**believable

Some examples of negative prefixes are: un-, dis-, mis-, non-, in-, anti-, im-, ir-, mal-, ab-.

A Choose the correct prefix to make each word negative.

un-   dis-   de-   mis-   non-   ab-   in-   anti-   il-   im-   ir-   mal-

practical	sure	legal	agree
complete	responsible	take	existent
hydrated	gravity	function	normal

B Write each word next to the correct meaning.

misinformed   unstable   insignificant   deflated   illegible   discontented

1. Sad or not happy: _____
2. To have no air: _____
3. Hard to read: _____
4. Not important: _____
5. Not secure, could fall over: _____
6. To be given the wrong information: _____

C Complete these by adding a negative prefix to the word in brackets.

1. Our school has an _____ (bullying) policy to care for the children.
2. The scientist had to _____ (contaminate) her lab after the explosion.
3. I stared in _____ (belief) as the car flew overhead.
4. I have _____ (placed) my school bag. Have you seen it?
5. A news report about a famine showed _____ (nourished) children.

Grammar – Commas

We use **commas** to separate lists of nouns or adjectives in a sentence. The word before 'and' does not need a comma after it. Neither does the last word in a list.

Examples: My friends Sinéad, James and Rebecca came to visit me yesterday.

The big, strong, hairy elephant stomped through the jungle.

We also use **commas** to separate lists of actions.

Example: We sweep the floor, tidy our desks and stack our chairs before we go home from school.

A In your copy, rewrite these using commas where appropriate.

1. My favourite sandwich is bacon lettuce tomato and cheese.

2. The shiny red fire engine raced to put out the hot blazing fire.

3. The weather in Ireland can be cold wet and windy all year round.

4. On yard, Leo likes to skip play football talk to his friends and check on his little brother.

5. Poland France Ireland Germany and Romania are all countries in Europe.

6. Mum asked me to tidy my room do the dishes sweep the floor and feed the dog.

B Complete these using a comma to separate at least three nouns, adjectives or actions.

1. My friends' names are _____.

2. Phillipa's dress is _____.

3. At the park, I _____.

We use **commas** to separate speech in a sentence. The comma must be placed inside the speech marks if the spoken text is **split**.

Example: "Those are my glasses," exclaimed Sennan, "lying on the floor."

C In your copy, rewrite these using commas where appropriate.

1. "We are going to the beach tomorrow" said Mrs Lee to her children.

2. "I'm tired" yawned Liam "so I should go to bed early."

3. "Storm Jessica is on its way" announced the newsreader "bringing heavy rain."

4. "I would like fruit a yoghurt and a sandwich for lunch, please" said Lucy.

D Dictation: Listen to your teacher and write the sentences in your copy.

 I can do this!   I'm getting there.   I need help!

Oral Language

A Alphabet game

In pairs, think about the treats and fun activities that might be at Timothy's party.

Version 1

Make a list. Start at 'a' and try to name something beginning with each letter of the alphabet, e.g **a**pple, **b**anana, **c**lown, etc.

Version 2

Pupil A names something they think could be at the party. Pupil B then names something beginning with the last letter of Pupil A's word, e.g. monke**y**, **y**ellow balloon**s**, **s**nake, etc.

Dear Anna,

You are invited to my birthday party next Saturday.

There will be lots of treats, party games and exciting things to do. I really hope you can make it.

Please write back by this Friday to let me know if you can come.

Sincerely,

Timothy

Writing Genre – To Socialise

The purpose of a **text used to socialise** is to maintain or improve relationships or to send a message from the sender to the recipient. A socialising text may be formal or informal.

Structure:

- **Orientation** – The reason for contact. It can also include a greeting or time and place.
- **Body** – Contains the main 'message'.
- **Prompt** – Includes instructions about what to do next.

A Write an e-mail to the Big, Bad Wolf.

Imagine that you are the oldest Pigg brother. Write an e-mail to the wolf inviting him to your home. Explain that you would like a chance to discuss what happened.

1. Plan your e-mail under the following headings:
   - Orientation – Reason for contact
   - Body – Main message you would like to convey
   - Prompt – Include an RSVP (how and when the wolf should respond).
   - Don't forget to include a greeting and farewell.

2. Write the first draft of your e-mail to the wolf using your plan. Use the invitation above to help you with the correct layout.

B Drama: courtroom scene

The meeting between the wolf and the oldest Pigg brother did not go well. The matter has now gone to court to decide who was in the wrong. In groups of six, act out the courtroom scene. Include the pig, the wolf, a judge and three jurors to decide the outcome.

Thank-you Letter

Comprehension Strategies

A Before reading: Changing predictions

Use the strategy of **Predicting**. In pairs, look at the title and illustration and predict what the text will be about. "I think this text will be about … because …"

Next, look at the key vocabulary below and make a new prediction based on this.

Jane	dress	mauve	frilly socks	adore	Aunty Grace
terrible	charming	ghastly	lovely surprise	birthday	Erk!

"My prediction has changed. Now I think this text will be about … because …"

B During reading: Contradicting language

Use the strategy of **Clarifying**. Some of the descriptive language in section A is contradictory. As you read, find the words in the text and explain to your partner why this is so.

C During reading: Just like me

Use the strategy of **Making Connections**. Stop along the way to make connections with the text.

- This reminds me of … because …
- I felt like this when …
- Something similar happened to me when …
- I think that Jane is feeling … because of the time I …

> I felt like this when …

D After reading: Character profile

Use the strategy of **Inferring**. Create a character profile for Jane using information from the text.

Likes	Dislikes
▪ _____	▪ _____
▪ _____	▪ _____
▪ _____	▪ _____
Personality	**Other information**
▪ _____	▪ _____
▪ _____	▪ _____
▪ _____	▪ _____

Comprehension

STOP! Use your dictionary to find out the meaning of the **bold** words below.

Underline all of the rhyming words that you can find in the poem. Then, highlight each group of rhyming words in a different colour.

Thank-you Letter

Dear Aunty Grace, ~~Mum said I had to~~
I'm writing this letter just to say
~~I hate that terrible dress you sent~~
I **adore** the dress you sent today.

~~Erk! Mauve!~~ The colour's just terrific!
Those little puff sleeves are really neat!
Frilly socks to match! It's just too much!
~~I'd rather wear blisters on my feet!~~

Mum says the dress looks sweetly **charming**.
It suits me now I'm growing up.
~~When I was made to try that thing on~~
~~I totally felt like throwing up!~~

The **lace** around the hem's ~~a nightmare —~~
~~I won't wear that ghastly dress!~~ a dream!
I've never seen such pretty **ruffles**.
~~I hope I wake up before I scream!~~

You shouldn't have spent so much money,
but thanks for such a lovely surprise —
~~of all the dum dum birthday presents,~~
~~yours, Aunty Grace, easily takes first prize!~~

You're very **generous**. ~~With some luck~~
~~I can lose the socks.~~ So thanks again
~~ink spilled on mauve I hope it won't wash out~~
for the wonderful dress! Love from

Jane XX

By Robin Klein

A In your copy, go investigate. 🔍

1. Who is writing this thank-you letter and who is she writing it to?
2. Why did Aunty Grace send the dress to Jane?
3. How did Jane react when she tried on the dress?
4. Describe the outfit that Aunty Grace has sent to Jane.
5. How does Jane intend on making sure that she won't have to wear the outfit?

B In your copy, give your opinion. 💭

1. Why do you think Jane is really writing this thank-you letter?
2. What kind of clothes do you think Jane usually wears? Explain.
3. Do you think Aunty Grace knows Jane well? Explain.
4. Do you think Aunty Grace will believe this thank-you letter is sincere? Explain.
5. What would you do if you had been sent a present that you didn't like?
6. Describe an outfit that you would hate to receive as a present.

C Vocabulary: Write the correct homophone. ✏️

look	luck	presents	presence	cent	sent	scent

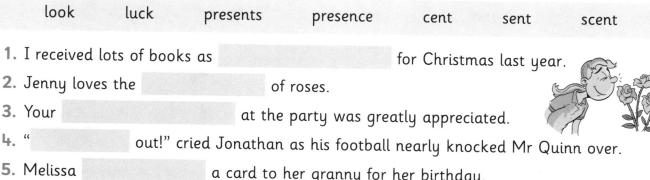

1. I received lots of books as _____ for Christmas last year.
2. Jenny loves the _____ of roses.
3. Your _____ at the party was greatly appreciated.
4. "_____ out!" cried Jonathan as his football nearly knocked Mr Quinn over.
5. Melissa _____ a card to her granny for her birthday.
6. Some European countries are discontinuing the one and two _____ coins.
7. It was only by _____ that I found my missing wallet.

D Cloze procedure: 'Aunty Grace's Reply'. Fill in the blanks.

Dear _____ ,

What a lovely letter to receive. I am glad to hear that you like the _____ I sent you. _____ is my favourite colour and I'm delighted that you like it _____ . I especially loved the _____ socks that came with it. Christmas is coming up soon and I _____ love to take you shopping for a pair of _____ to match. Now that you're getting _____ , it's about time we got you out of those jeans and runners and _____ something a little more ladylike.

Lots of love,

_____ Grace xxx

Phonics – Silent Letters

Silent letters are letters that we do not pronounce when reading or saying words, e.g. sign. They are important for spelling and to help us tell the difference between some words.

A Tick the correct spelling of each word and ring the silent letter/s.

gnaw	cemist	autum	pterodactyl	castle
naw	chemist	autumn	terodactyl	casle
biscit	scissors	drout	iland	thistle
biscuit	sissors	drought	island	thisle
fite	colum	balley	gard	receipt
fight	column	ballet	guard	receit

B Complete the words by inserting the correct silent letter.

'b', 'd', 'k', 'h' and 'l' are all common silent letters.

1. Maham is a great dancer, because she has good r___ythm.

2. The plum___er fixed our shower last We___nesday.

3. The mechanic had to scrap my ve___icle, as it wasn't safe to drive.

4. Mr Henderson used his han___kerchief to clean my ___nee when I fell.

5. The rescuer helped the man to stay ca___m when he got stuck clim___ing the cliff.

6. "I wou___d like to learn how to ___nit," admitted Harry.

C In your copy, write a short story using as many silent-letter words as you can. Use some of the words above to help you.

Grammar – Pronouns

A **pronoun** is a word that takes the place of one or more nouns.

A **personal pronoun** replaces people or things (I, they, that), e.g. **Lily** gave me **the book**. → **She** gave **it** to me.

A **possessive pronoun** shows ownership (mine, theirs). It is placed after or instead of the noun, e.g. That bicycle is **Stefan's**. → That bicycle is **his**.

A **possessive adjective** describes who or what owns the noun (my, their). It is placed before the noun, e.g. That is **Stefan's** bicycle. → That is **his** bicycle.

> **Top tip!**
>
> Most possessive prounouns end in 's', e.g. our home → ours.

A **Underline the pronouns in these sentences. Choose six and place each in the correct category in the table.**

Hint: Most sentences have more than one pronoun.

1. I knew the car was ours, because I recognised its cracked windscreen.
2. "Hey! You can't have that. It's mine!" Antonio shouted at his brother.
3. She loves to travel to new places with her family.
4. They liked our performance, but I preferred theirs.
5. Were you looking for these?
6. "Lucy, is this yours?" asked Victor.

> **Remember!**
>
> A possessive prounoun **replaces** the noun, while a possessive adjective **describes** it.

Personal Pronoun	Possessive Pronoun	Possessive Adjective

B **Complete these using the correct pronouns.**

| any | ourselves | several | both | he | none | her |

1. When the shopkeeper showed me two lovely dresses, I bought   .
2. Nia asked   friend for a chewing gum, but she had   .
3. After the school concert, we were very proud of   .
4. I lost my pencil. Do you have   ?
5. While Nick was picking strawberries,   ate   .

C **Dictation: Listen to your teacher and write the sentences in your copy.**

 I can do this!   I'm getting there.   I need help!

Oral Language

A False thank-you letters

In pairs, write a thank-you letter similar to the poem on page 32. Think about what you received, the nice things you could say about it and what you don't like about it. Before you begin, brainstorm some vocabulary that you might need. After you have written it, perform it for the class. Each of you should take a different part and match your voice to what you are saying.

Writing Genre – To Socialise

The **language of a text used to socialise** should include:

- first- and second-person pronouns, e.g. I, you, we.
- a specific subject, e.g. Aunty Grace, Mr Pigg.
- questions or statements of inquiry, e.g. How are you?
- simple past tense, e.g. When I tried it on …
- action verbs, e.g. visited, arranged.
- words to show time, e.g. then, next week.
- a formal or informal tone, depending on the audience, e.g. See you soon, Yours sincerely.

A Review, edit and rewrite your e-mail from the oldest Pigg brother to the Big, Bad Wolf.

1. Read over your e-mail and think about the following:
   - The tone of your message
   - Which version of the story you agree with
   - Do you feel guilty and want to explain?
   - Or are you angry with the wolf and want him to apologise?

2. Make sure that your e-mail has all of the following:
   - Orientation
   - Body
   - Prompt
   - A greeting and a farewell
   - A suitable or clever e-mail address for the pig
   - Language used to socialise

3. Read over your e-mail and edit it for spelling, punctuation and grammar.

4. Rewrite your e-mail.

5. Check your work using the to socialise self-assessment checklist.

B Drama

Practise reading out the poem 'Thank-you Letter' in different voices to suit the tone of what Jane is writing. Read it all together and then in two parts. Split the class in half and have your teacher decide which group is the most convincing.

'Luncheon of the Boating Party'

7

Comprehension Strategies

A Before reading: Five senses

Use the strategy of **Visualising**. Look at the picture and imagine that you are one of the characters. Record what you can see, hear, smell, taste and touch.

B During reading

Use the strategy of **Clarifying**. We need to have something clarified when we read a word, a phrase or an idea that we don't understand. Here are some steps to help you clarify:

- Read back.
- Read on.
- Think of your schema. Do you have background knowledge that might help?
- Is there any information in the image that might help?
- Might another phrase make sense here?

C After reading: Fact or fib?

Use the strategy of **Synthesising**. Write three facts and one fib about the text. Then, in pairs, swap your lists and find each other's fib.

Facts

1. _____

   _____

2. _____

   _____

3. _____

   _____

4. _____

   _____

Comprehension

 Use your dictionary to find out the meaning of the **bold** words below.

'Luncheon of the Boating Party'

By Pierre-Auguste Renoir (painted during 1880–1881)

Pierre-Auguste Renoir was a French painter. He helped to **found** the **Impressionist** art movement in the 1870s. Impressionism broke many artistic rules at the time and was very unpopular at first. Impressionist painters **favoured** broken brushstrokes over detail to create movement and light in their paintings. They **focused** on scenes of modern life and often painted outdoors rather than in a studio which was more **common** at the time.

'**Luncheon** of the Boating Party' portrays a group of Renoir's friends relaxing on a restaurant balcony **overlooking** the River Seine in Paris. This painting **reflects** a change in French society at the time, as it includes people from different social classes. Among the partygoers are an art **historian**, a poet, an actress, artists and Renoir's future wife, **seamstress** Aline Charigot. The painting **combines** still life, figures and landscape, **demonstrating** Renoir's wide range of artistic skills.

A In your copy, go investigate.

1. Who painted this painting?
2. During what time of year was this painting composed? Explain your answer.
3. How many people can you see in this painting? Look closely.
4. What can you see in the background beyond the tent?
5. Describe the clothing of the people in the painting. Are they all dressed the same?
6. What are these people doing? What tells you this?

B In your copy, give your opinion. ?

1. What do you think these people were doing before this scene was painted?
2. Why might the two men near the front be dressed differently from everyone else?
3. Look at the three people to the right in the background. What do you think is happening?
4. Does anyone else look like they are not enjoying the party? Explain your answer.
5. Why was Impressionism unpopular when it was first introduced? Do you agree?
6. Do you like this painting? Why/Why not?

C Vocabulary

Write sentences using some of the bold words in the text. Use your dictionary to help you. Choose a number to challenge yourself.

D Cloze procedure: 'Pierre-Auguste Renoir'. Fill in the blanks.

Pierre-Auguste Renoir was _____ in France in 1841. He became a porcelain painter as a teenager. During this time, he attended free drawing classes. His family lived near the famous art museum, the Louvre, and _____ learned to paint by copying the paintings there. In 1862, he entered a famous _____ school. At the beginning of his career, he struggled to make money. He lived _____ friends and occasionally didn't have enough _____ to buy paint. In 1871, he and _____ friends Camille Pissaro, Claude Monet, Paul Cézanne and Edgar Degas started the Impressionist art _____ by exhibiting their works in Paris. The name came from a review that made fun of their paintings, saying that they were only 'impressions' of paintings, as _____ had less detail than the style at the _____. The Impressionists struggled to gain respect for many years. However, by the time of his _____ in 1919, Renoir was world-renowned. He left behind over two hundred _____ of art that have served as inspiration for many famous _____.

Phonics – '-tion'

'-**tion**' makes the /**shun**/ sound, e.g. sta**tion**.

The suffix '-**tion**' is often added to **verbs** to make **nouns**.

Verbs ending in 't' and 'e'

- If the verb ends in '**t**', only add '-**ion**', e.g. to act → ac**tion**.
- If the verb ends in '**e**', remove this before adding '-**tion**', e.g. to produce → produc**tion**.
- Sometimes the '**e**' changes to '**i**' before '-**tion**', e.g. to compete → compet**ition**.

With words ending in '**stion**', the **ti** makes a /**ch**/ sound, e.g. sugges**tion**.

A Write the correct '-tion' word below each picture.

| exclamation | competition | incantation | location | animation |
| celebration | eruption | pollination | injection | investigation |

B Use '-tion' to change each root verb to a noun.

1. to oppose _____opposition_____   2. to connect _____
3. to produce _____   4. to quest _____
5. to contribute _____   6. to introduce _____
7. to suggest _____   8. to direct _____
9. to opt _____   10. to substitute _____

C Ring the correct '-tion' words to complete these.

1. The doctor told me that I had an ear **infection** / **section**.

2. There is very little **distraction** / **nutrition** in sugary foods.

3. Alice overheard her mother **mention** / **condition** her birthday present.

4. "What is the **function** / **demolition** of your **subscription** / **invention**?" asked the judge.

Grammar – Singular and Plural

'**Singular**' means one. '**Plural**' means more than one. There are different rules for changing nouns from singular to plural.

- For most words, just add and '**s**'.
- Words ending in a consonant and then '**y**': change the '**y**' to '**ies**'.
- Words ending in '**s**', '**x**', '**zz**', '**sh**', '**ch**', '**ss**' or a consonant and then '**o**': add '**es**'.
- Words ending in '**f**' or '**fe**': remove the '**f** or '**fe**' and add '**ves**'.
- Some words are irregular and don't change at all.
- Other words have a completely different spelling when plural.

cat → cats
sky → skies

buzz → buzzes

calf → calves
sheep → sheep
foot → feet

A Change each word from singular to plural.

1. monkey _____
2. bag _____
3. box _____
4. loaf _____
5. tomato _____
6. fly _____

B Write the plural for each irregular noun below the picture.

When changing nouns in sentences to plural, it is important to remember that other words such as pronouns and verbs might need to change too.

Examples: The teacher reads us a story every day. → The teachers **read** us stories every day. The man is wearing his coat. → The **men are** wearing **their** coats.

C Change these sentences to their plural form. Make sure the pronouns and verbs agree with the nouns.

1. The (woman) _____ (cleans) _____ (her) _____ (glass) _____ every day.
2. (This) _____ (mouse) _____ (likes) _____ to eat cheese.
3. The (cat) _____ (loves) _____ (its) _____ new (toy) _____ .
4. (I) _____ (am) _____ growing (flower) _____ in (my) _____ garden.

D Dictation: Listen to your teacher and write the sentences in your copy.

I can do this!   I'm getting there.   I need help!

41

Oral Language

A Alliteration poems

Alliteration is a literary style in which two or more words in a row have the same beginning consonant sound, e.g. fat fish. Sit in a circle and compose a class alliteration poem. Each person contributes one line, which begins with a name and a verb that alliterate.

Example: **The Picnic**

Amelia ate sandwiches in the shade.

Ben brought fizzy drinks.

Carrie complained that it was cold.

Writing Genre – Poetry Writing

A **poem** is a fictional piece of writing that entertains the reader. A poet uses words and images to share personal thoughts or feelings about a subject. There are many different forms of poetry. Some poems, such as acrostic poems, limericks and rhyming couplets have very distinctive structures, while free-verse poems have none.

A Cinquain poetry

A cinquain has five lines and does not need to rhyme. Its structure means that it has a diamond shape. Below are the rules for writing a cinquain, along with an example.

1st line: one word (the title)	**Sun**
2nd line: two related adjectives	Bright, hot
3rd line: three descriptive '–ing' verbs	Shimmering, shining, burning
4th line: one complete sentence	It gives life to our home.
5th line: one word (related to the title)	Star

Write a cinquain of your own.

- Think of something that you are interested in and would like to write about.
- Brainstorm some words and phrases to do with your idea.
- Think about a story that you want to tell in your poem.
- Try to include descriptions, actions and feelings and a conclusion.
- Write your cinquain using the ideas from your brainstorm, in an order that tells your story.
- Draw a picture to accompany your poem.

B Art activity

Study the works of impressionist artists Pierre-Auguste Renoir, Claude Monet, Edgar Degas and Paul Cézanne. Paint a still life or a landscape using their style of bright colours and broken brushstrokes.

Revision and Assessment 8

Revision: Grammar and Phonics

Look back at the grammar on pages 5, 11, 17, 23, 29, 35 and 41.

Day 1

1. Ring the words that need a capital letter and add the missing punctuation.

   (a) did amal celebrate eid in september

   (b) ouch i cut my knee

2. Tick for the underlined word.

   (a) Sonia sings <u>beautifully</u>.

   | Noun | Verb |
   | Adverb | Pronoun |

   (b) Unicorns are imaginary <u>creatures</u>.

   | Noun | Verb |
   | Adverb | Pronoun |

3. Change these words to plural.

   (a) glass _____ (b) tooth _____

   (c) leaf _____ (d) fox _____

4. Tick the correct homophone.

   (a) There are _____ many people here.

   to   too   two

   (b) They have lost _____ coats.

   there   they're   their

5. Add the suffix. (ing, ed, ful, y)

   (a) fun _____ (b) beauty _____

   (c) sing _____ (d) change _____

6. Add the negative prefix.

   (a) ____responsible

   (b) ____agree

7. Ring the correct spelling.

   (a) sewage / sewege

   (b) recyclible / recyclable

   (c) opposition / opposishun

Day 2

1. Ring the words that need a capital letter and add the missing punctuation.

   (a) i visited france spain and germany

   (b) i am reading *the hobbit* said tom

2. Tick for the underlined word.

   (a) I bought <u>both</u>.

   | Noun | Verb |
   | Adverb | Pronoun |

   (b) You should <u>clean</u> your room.

   | Noun | Verb |
   | Adverb | Pronoun |

3. Change these words to plural.

   (a) king _____ (b) sheep _____

   (c) fly _____ (d) church _____

4. Tick the correct homophone.

   (a) Can I have a _____ of cake?

   piece   peace

   (b) This is a _____ of time.

   waste   waist

5. Add the suffix. (ness, est, ship, ous)

   (a) big _____ (b) lazy _____

   (c) friend _____ (d) fame _____

6. Add the negative prefix.

   (a) ____legal

   (b) ____existent

7. Ring the correct spelling.

   (a) privilege / privilage

   (b) flexable / flexible

   (c) opposition / opposishun

Revision: Grammar and Phonics

Day 3

1. Ring the words that need a capital letter and add the missing punctuation.

    (a) the *star wars* films are great

    (b) i'll come with you   said mariam

2. Match the underlined words.

    <u>Paul</u> can play the <u>guitar</u>.

    Common noun: _____

    Proper noun: _____

3. Insert the helping verb.

    (a) I _____ clean my room tomorrow.

    (b) Cassy _____ not like fish.

4. Change the adjectives to adverbs.

    (a) lucky _____

    (b) beautiful _____

5. Match to the type of prounoun: mine, they

    (a) Personal pronoun: _____

    (b) Possessive pronoun: _____

6. Make the verb agree.

    (a) The <u>men</u> (runs) _____ down the road.

    (b) The <u>cats</u> (is) _____ chasing the mice.

7. Tick the correct homophone.

    (a) I can't _____ you.

       hear [ ]   here [ ]

    (b) _____ a talented artist.

       your [ ]   you're [ ]

8. Add the negative prefix.

    (a) ____function (b) ____agree

9. Ring the silent letter.

    (a) thumb (b) chalk (c) answer

Day 4

1. Ring the words that need a capital letter and add the missing punctuation.

    (a) oh no i ripped my jeans

    (b) my friends are arthur george and dara

2. Match the noun gender: chair, king, sibling, niece

    (a) Feminine: _____

    (b) Masculine: _____

    (c) Common: _____

    (d) Neuter: _____

3. Match to the type of adjective: angrily, soon, around

    (a) time _____

    (b) manner _____

    (c) place _____

4. Make the pronoun agree.

    (a) The <u>boys</u> do (his) _____ homework.

    (b) <u>We</u> lost (my) _____ coats.

5. Tick the correct homophone.

    (a) The dog ate _____ bone.

       it's [ ]   its [ ]

    (b) I had a long _____ at the doctor's.

       weight [ ]   wait [ ]

6. Ring the correct spelling.

    (a) heritege / heritage

    (b) changeable / changeible

7. Make '-tion' nouns from the verbs.

    (a) To exclaim: _____

    (b) To erupt: _____

Assessment: Phonics

A Ring the correct spelling.

1. My sister has a **beautyful / beautiful** singing voice.
2. Killian would like to study science in **collage / college**.
3. I **quickened / quickkened** my pace as it began to get dark.
4. Scott makes sure to buy items in **recyclable / recyclibe** packaging.
5. I won a trophy at my hip-hop dancing **competition / competetion**.
6. Cara got the **bigest / biggest** piece of cake at her birthday party.
7. I am at a **disadvantage / disadvantege** in basketball, because I'm short.
8. Ugh! This yoghurt is **inedible / inedable**.
9. Well done, Victoria, that is a great **suggestion / suggesion**.
10. I am **smileing / smiling** in my baby photos.

10

B Insert the correct homophone.

1. _____ are nine sides on a nonagon. **there/their/they're**
2. Always do _____ best work in school. **you're/your**
3. I tied the belt around my _____. **waste/waist**
4. _____ a beautiful day outside. **it's/its**
5. I won a gold _____ at the sports day. **medal/meddle**
6. We are not _____ to chew gum in school. **aloud/allowed**
7. It's _____ hot in here. Open a window. **to/too/two**
8. Did you _____ what I said? **here/hear**
9. Our teacher _____ us how to play the tin whistle. **taught/taut**
10. Angelo and Darragh ride _____ bikes to school. **there/their/they're**

10

C Ring the silent letter.

1. gnome   2. salmon   3. pneumonia   4. solemn   5. design
6. sword   7. plumber   8. calm   9. reign   10. knead

10

D Write the correct prefix.

| un- | de- | mis- | ab- | in- | anti- | il- | im- | ir- | mal- |

1. ____ take   2. ____ complete   3. ____ hydrated   4. ____ sure
5. ____ normal   6. ____ practical 7. ____ function   8. ____ gravity

8

Assessment: Comprehension

The Fox and the Stork – an Aesop's Fable

There once lived a cruel fox and a clever stork. The two were neighbours and often bickered over silly things.

One day, the fox decided to play a trick on the stork. He invited her over for dinner, telling her not to eat anything that day as he was preparing a feast for her. He slaved in his kitchen for hours and hours, chopping vegetables, cutting meat, keeping the fire at just the right temperature, stirring and stirring the contents of the great big pot.

When the stork arrived, the fox gleefully asked her to take a seat at the table while he served up dinner. The stork and the fox toasted to being good neighbours with fresh lemonade and the fox tucked in. The stew was delicious! He lapped up every last morsel of food with his long tongue. But the stork didn't touch her food. Her long beak pecked at the plate, but her tongue could not reach it. The cruel fox had served dinner on shallow plates, meaning that the stork's long beak prevented her from eating. However, the stork was a proud bird and didn't complain. She thanked the fox for the delicious meal and invited him over for dinner the following day to repay him for his hospitality.

The fox arrived the next evening, his mouth watering at the aroma that reached his nostrils as soon as he walked in the door. He sat down at the table, eagerly awaiting the meal. The stork placed his dinner in front of him and tucked into her own, pretending not to notice the angry look on the fox's face. She had made her own stew and served it in tall, narrow

beakers. Her long beak fit perfectly into the beaker and she was able to suck up the delicious food. The fox, however, could not fit his thick snout into the beaker and his tongue was not long enough to reach. The fox knew that he had been outsmarted and didn't say anything to the stork. He thanked her for a delicious meal as he left the house with his stomach rumbling. He knew now how cruel his trick had been and he never played such a trick on the stork, or anyone else, ever again.

Assessment: Comprehension and Vocabulary

A **In your copy, go investigate.**

1. Explain why the author says, 'the fox <u>gleefully</u> asked' the stork to take a seat.
2. Why did the stork play a trick on the fox?
3. Why could the fox not eat his dinner at the stork's house?
4. Was the fox hungry leaving the stork's house? How do you know?
5. Describe the fox's character. Use evidence from the text.
6. What do you think the moral (lesson) of 'The Fox and the Stork' is?

6

B **Vocabulary: Match each word with its meaning.**

| dice | presents | seismologist | presence | submerged |

1. A scientist who studies earthquakes _____
2. In attendance or company _____
3. A cooking term meaning to cut into small cubes _____
4. Gifts given on birthdays _____
5. Completely covered, usually with water _____

5

C **Match each word with its abbreviation.**

1. road ▪   ▪ messrs   2. doctor ▪   ▪ mrs
3. refrigerator ▪   ▪ st   4. aeroplane ▪   ▪ cllr
5. street ▪   ▪ rd   6. councillor ▪   ▪ dr
7. misters ▪   ▪ fridge   8. missus ▪   ▪ plane

8

D **Cloze procedure: 'Christmas Shopping'. Fill in the blanks.**

It was _____ and Andrew and Shauna were shopping for presents.

"Hey!" said Andrew. "Dad would love this remote-_____ helicopter."

"I don't think _____," said Shauna. "What about this nail-painting set for Mum?"

"But Mum never paints her _____," replied Andrew.

Suddenly, Shauna's eyes lit up, as _____ spied something across the shopping _____. "Come on," she said. "I know exactly _____ to get them."

On Christmas morning, _____ and Shauna watched with delight as Mum and _____ opened _____ present; a framed photograph of Andrew and Shauna pulling silly faces.

10

47

Assessment: Grammar

A In each of the sentences below:

1. Ring the words that need a capital letter.

2. Add the missing punctuation.

3. Find a noun, a verb, an adverb and a pronoun.

   (a) did they wake up early on christmas morning

   (b) she quickly read *gangsta granny* before returning it to the library

   (c) he ate sandwiches yoghurt grapes and an apple yesterday

Capital letters ☐ 6

Punctuation ☐ 7

Noun	Verb	Adverb	Pronoun

☐ 12

B Ring the mistake/s in each sentence.

1. Rachel walked to the shop with his brother.

2. We have tree dogs and two fishes.

3. She sings beautiful.

4. There are too many flys in my room. They is really annoying me.

5. The dog lost it's bone.

6. My dentist's name is Barry. She fixes my tooths.

7. Eve, Natalie and Jenny are my friend. He come to my house every day.

☐ 11

C Change each word to plural.

1. kiss _____

2. sky _____

3. basket _____

4. foot _____

5. life _____

6. man _____

☐ 6

D Insert a helping verb.

1. Pandas like _____ eat bamboo plants.

2. Tomorrow, I _____ ride my bike to school.

3. My baby brother _____ walk without falling now.

☐ 3

E Dictation: Listen to your teacher and write the sentences in your copy.

 I can do this!   I'm getting there.   I need help!

Back to the Burrow

Comprehension Strategies

A Before reading: Pre-reading summaries

In groups of three, use the strategies of **Summarising**, **Inferring** and **Predicting**.

- Divide the story into three parts. Assign each part to a pupil in the group.
- Each pupil reads only their section and writes a one-line summary.
- After this, use what you have read to infer what happened in the story before your section and to predict what will happen next.
- Each pupil reads out their own summary and the group pieces together each sentence to make a six-line summary.
- Compare your inferences and predictions with the summaries in your group.
- Compare your summaries with those of other groups and to the story once you have finished reading.

B After reading: Story map

Use the strategies of **Summarising** and **Determining Importance**. Complete the story map. Are you left with any questions?

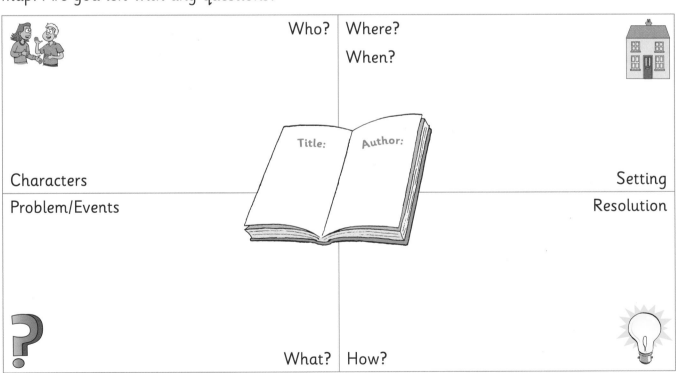

Who? | Where? When?

Characters

Problem/Events

Title: | Author:

Setting

Resolution

What? | How?

C After reading: What's my point of view?

Use the strategy of **Synthesising**. As a class, record the key events in the story. Split into groups, assigning one character from the story to each group. In your group, discuss how your character felt during each event. Finally, make new groups containing each character so that everyone hears the point of view of each character.

Comprehension

STOP! Use your dictionary to find out the meaning of the **bold** words below.

Back to the Burrow

"Off you go then, Fred," said Mr Weasley.

"Coming," said Fred. "Oh no – hang on –"

A bag of sweets had spilled out of Fred's pocket and the **contents** were now rolling in every direction – big, fat toffees in brightly coloured wrappers. Fred **scrambled** around, **cramming** them back into his pocket, then gave the Dursleys a cheery wave, stepped forward and walked right into the fire, saying, "The Burrow!" Aunt Petunia gave a little **shuddering** gasp. There was a **whooshing** sound, and Fred **vanished** …

"See you," said Harry, putting one foot forward into the green flames, which felt **pleasantly** like warm breath. At that moment, however, a horrible **gagging** sound **erupted** behind him, and Aunt Petunia started to scream. Harry **wheeled** round. Dudley was no longer standing behind his parents. He was kneeling beside the coffee table, and he was gagging and **spluttering** on a foot-long, purple, slimy thing that was **protruding** from his mouth. One **bewildered** second later, Harry realised that the foot-long thing was Dudley's tongue – and that a brightly coloured toffee wrapper lay on the floor before him. Aunt Petunia **hurled** herself onto the ground beside Dudley, **seized** the end of his **swollen** tongue and **attempted** to **wrench** it out of his mouth; unsurprisingly, Dudley yelled and spluttered worse than ever, trying to fight her off. Uncle Vernon was **bellowing** and waving his arms around, and Mr Weasley had to shout to make himself heard.

"Not to worry, I can sort him out!" he yelled, **advancing** on Dudley with his wand **outstretched**, but Aunt Petunia screamed worse than ever and threw herself on top of Dudley, shielding him from Mr Weasley.

"No, really!" said Mr Weasley **desperately**. "It's a simple process – it was the toffee – my son Fred – real practical joker – but it's only an **Engorgement** Charm – at least, I think it is – please, I can correct it –"

But far from being **reassured**, the Dursleys became more panic-stricken; Aunt Petunia was sobbing **hysterically**, tugging Dudley's tongue as though **determined** to rip it out; Dudley appeared to be to be **suffocating** under the combined pressure of his mother and his tongue, and Uncle Vernon, who had lost control completely, seized a china figure from on top of the sideboard, and threw it very hard at Mr Weasley, who ducked, causing the ornament to **shatter** in the blasted fireplace.

(From '*Harry Potter and the Goblet of Fire*' by J. K. Rowling)

A In your copy, go investigate.

1. What happened to delay Fred's departure from the Dursleys' house?
2. How did Fred leave the Dursleys' house?
3. What made Harry turn around?
4. Describe Dudley's tongue.
5. How did this happen to him?
6. How did Aunt Petunia try to help Dudley?

B In your copy, give your opinion.

1. Do you think Fred dropped the sweets on purpose? Explain.
2. Do you think Dudley deserved this happening to him? Why/Why not?
3. What do you think is Aunt Petunia's opinion of magic? Explain.
4. What do you think Mr Weasley was going to do to 'correct' Dudley's tongue?
5. What would you have done if you were Vernon Dursley in this situation?
6. Describe what you think happens next.

C Vocabulary

Defined characters are important for a narrative. In your copy, choose a character from the text and complete a character profile like the one below.

D Cloze procedure: 'J. K. Rowling'. Fill in the blanks.

J. K. Rowling is an English _____, best known for writing the 'Harry _____' series. She was born Joanne Rowling, but was advised to use _____ initials by publishers, because it was thought that the target audience of boys would not want to read a book _____ by a woman. In 1990, while on-board a delayed train, the story of a young wizard came to _____ and she began writing immediately. She finished writing '_____ Potter and the Philosopher's Stone' in 1995, but it was rejected by twelve publishers. Finally, Bloomsbury decided to publish the _____, because the chairman's daughter enjoyed the story so _____. There are seven books in the 'Harry Potter' series in total. They have _____ many awards and sold more than 400 million copies worldwide, making _____ the best-selling series in history.

Phonics – '-sion'

Like '-**tion**', '-**sion**' makes the /**shun**/ sound, e.g. man**sion**.

The '**si**' can sometimes make a /**zh**/ instead of a /**sh**/ sound, e.g. ver**sion**.

The suffix '-**sion**' is often added to verbs to make nouns.

'-**sion**' is mostly added to verbs ending in '**s**', '**se**', '**d**' or '**de**'.

These are all removed before adding '-**sion**', e.g. to colli**de** → colli**sion**.

A Match each '-sion' word to its root verb. Use a dictionary to help you.

1. misapprehension ▪   ▪ to expel
2. extension ▪   ▪ to comprehend
3. expulsion ▪   ▪ to expand
4. comprehension ▪   ▪ to misapprehend
5. expansion ▪   ▪ to extend

6. suspension ▪   ▪ to tense
7. immersion ▪   ▪ to propel
8. pretension ▪   ▪ to suspend
9. propulsion ▪   ▪ to immerse
10. tension ▪   ▪ to pretend

B Match each '-sion' word to its meaning.

| collision | diversion | mansion | pension | apprehension | revulsion |

1. A very large or impressive house _____
2. Money paid to a person who has retired from working _____
3. The act of coming violently into contact or crashing _____
4. A feeling of disgust _____
5. A detour on the road **or** a distraction _____
6. The act of understanding **or** a worry of future trouble _____

C Ring the correct spelling of the '-tion' and '-sion' words to complete these.

1. The **conversion / convertion** of euros to pounds can cause **confution / confusion**.

2. "A 3-D shape has three **dimensions / dimentions**," **mensioned / mentioned** my teacher.

3. I heard an **exclamasion / exclamation** of **revulsion / revultion** from my mother when she saw a rat.

4. The detective began an **investigation / investigasion** to decide which **vertion / version** of events was true.

5. "This is an **occasion / occation** for a **celebration / celebrasion**!" cried Rosie.

6. Indiana Jones has a strong **aversion / avertion** to snakes.

Grammar – Adjectives

An **adjective** is a word that describes a noun or a pronoun. It *usually* comes before the noun, e.g. It was a **hot** day, so I drank a **cold** drink. Adjectives make our writing more appealing, so it is important to use interesting ones, e.g.
It was a **sweltering** day, so I drank a **chilled** drink.

A **Underline the adjectives. Then, in your copy, replace each with a more interesting one. Use a thesaurus to help you.**

1. The big elephant was afraid of the small mouse.
2. Jamie's granny is old, but she bakes tasty cakes.
3. "I am tired," yawned the young boy.
4. I will wear my nice dress to the fancy party tonight.
5. "I don't want to play with Seán!" cried the scared boy. "He's mean."
6. "It is a hot day!" exclaimed Nancy as she took off her warm scarf.

Adjectives can be used to compare different nouns.
Positive adjectives describe one noun, e.g. The **small** mouse ran across the floor.
Comparative adjectives compare two of the same noun and are formed by adding '**er**' to the adjective, e.g. The small**er** mouse stole the cheese.
Superlative adjectives compare more than two of the same noun and are formed by adding '**est**' to the adjective, e.g. The small**est** mouse was hiding from the cat.

B **Complete the table below.**

Positive	Comparative	Superlative
	bigger	
greedy		
	simpler	
		clumsiest

Top tip!

If an adjective ends in '**e**', just add '**r**' or '**st**'.

If an adjective ends in '**y**', change it to '**i**' and then add '**er**' or '**est**'.

C **Change these nouns to adjectives.**

1. France _____French_____
2. safety _____
3. beauty _____
4. strength _____
5. peace _____
6. speed _____
7. Ireland _____
8. grace _____
9. mystery _____

D **Dictation: Listen to your teacher and write the sentences in your copy.**

 I can do this!   I'm getting there.   I need help!

Oral Language

A Character profiling

In pairs, look at the pictures and describe each character. Think about:

- Personality
- Family
- Hopes/goals
- Job/activities
- Likes/dislikes
- Strengths/weaknesses
- Favourite food/music/film, etc.

Writing Genre – Narrative Writing

A **narrative** is a fictional story written to entertain the reader.

Structure:

- **Setting** – Introduce the setting, time and main character. Set the mood/tone.
- **Series of events** – This involves an initiating event (how did the story start?) and a problem or conflict for the main character.
- **Resolution** – The problem is usually resolved for the main character.

A Plan, organise and write a narrative story in which something goes wrong for the main character due to magic.

1. In your copy, complete a character profile for your main character using a mind map like the one below.

2. Complete this story plan.

Setting:	Who?	Where?	When?
Initiating event:			
Problem:			
Resolution:			

3. Use the character profile and story plan to write the first draft of your narrative.

B Art activity: Design your own magical food.

Use coloured paper and various other materials to create the food packaging. Don't forget to think of a clever name and what effect the food has on those who eat it.

Yellow-spotted Lizards 10

Comprehension Strategies

A Before reading: Picture flick

Use the strategies of **Predicting** and **Questioning**. Look at the images next to the text. Make three predictions and write three questions that you have.

B During reading: Check your predictions and questions.

Were you right? Have any of your questions been answered?

C During reading: Tricky words

Use the strategy of **Word Attack**. Follow the steps on page vi at the beginning of the book when you come across tricky words in the text.

D During reading: Wow word wall

Use the strategy of **Word Attack**. Record your tricky words as you read and make a 'Wow word wall' as a class.

beam glanced	scramble suppress	commotion warden	occurred	illuminated

E After reading: I am the Warden …

Use the strategy of **Inferring**. Using evidence from the text, write a short paragraph about the Warden, written by her. Describe her personality and her childhood.

_____

_____

_____

_____

_____

_____

_____

_____

Comprehension

STOP! Use your dictionary to find out the meaning of the **bold** words below.

Yellow-spotted Lizards

"You boys arrived just in the nick —" the Warden started to say. She stopped talking and she stopped walking. Then she slowly backed away. A lizard had crawled up on top of the suitcase. Its big red eyes glowed in the **beam** of the flashlight. Its mouth was open, and Stanley could see its white tongue moving in and out between its black teeth.

Zero sat as still as a statue. A second lizard crawled up over the side of the suitcase and stopped less than an inch away from Zero's little finger. Stanley was afraid to look, and afraid not to. He wondered if he should try to **scramble** out of the hole before the lizards turned on him, but he didn't want to cause any **commotion**. The second lizard crawled across Zero's fingers and halfway up his arm. It **occurred** to Stanley that the lizards were probably on the suitcase when he handed it to Zero.

"There's another one!" gasped Mr Pendanski. He shined the flashlight on the box of Frosted Flakes, which lay on its side beside Stanley's hole. A lizard was crawling out of it. The light also **illuminated** Stanley's hole. He **glanced** downward and had to force himself to **suppress** a scream. He was standing in a lizard nest. He felt the scream explode inside him. He could see six lizards. There were three on the ground, two on his left leg, and one on his right sneaker. He tried to remain very still. Something was crawling up the back of his neck …

"What do we do?" asked Mr Pendanski.

"We wait," said the Warden. "It won't be very long."

"At least we'll have a body to give that woman," said Mr Pendanski.

"She's going to ask a lot of questions," said Mr Sir. […]

"Let her ask her questions," said the Warden. "Just so long as I have the suitcase, I don't care what happens. Do you know how long …" her voice **trailed off**, then started up again. "When I was little I'd watch my parents dig holes, every weekend and holidays. When I got bigger, I had to dig too. Even on Christmas."

Stanley felt tiny claws dig into the side of his face as the lizard pulled itself off his neck and up past his chin.

"It won't be long now," the Warden said.

Stanley could hear his heart beat. Each beat told him he was still alive, at least for one more second.

(From '*Holes*' by Louis Sachar

A In your copy, go investigate.

1. At the beginning of the story, why did the Warden stop talking?

2. Describe the lizards that were crawling over Stanley and Zero.

3. What was Zero holding?

4. What time of day was it? Explain.

5. How many lizards were in the hole with Stanley and Zero?

6. Where were Stanley and Zero standing?

B In your copy, give your opinion. {?}

1. How do you think Stanley and Zero got into this situation?

2. What do you think is in the suitcase?

3. Do you think the Warden is a kind person? Explain your answer.

4. Do you think the lizards are dangerous? What makes you think this?

5. What do you think the Warden meant by saying, "It won't be long now"?

6. What would you have done in this situation if you were Stanley?

C Vocabulary: Match each bold word/phrase from the text with its meaning below. Then, choose a number to challenge yourself and write a sentence for each in your copy.

1. Lit up _____
2. Looked quickly/briefly _____
3. Came to mind _____
4. Keep in or repress _____
5. Faded away _____
6. A noisy disturbance _____
7. A ray of light _____
8. To climb or move quickly on hands and feet _____

D Cloze procedure: 'Camp Green Lake'. Fill in the blanks.

There hasn't been a lake at Camp Green Lake for a very long _____ . Now, the Warden runs a juvenile detention centre from the barren, flat wasteland that _____ once the largest lake in Texas. The boys _____ are sent here as punishment for their crimes dig one hole, five-feet deep and five-_____ wide, a day. The _____ claims this _____ character building. It is a lie. Stanley Yelnats has been sent to _____ Green Lake or a crime he _____ not commit. When he and _____ friend Zero escape, they accidentally uncover a nest of the deadly yellow-spotted _____ , and the secret history of Camp Green Lake buried with it.

Phonics – '-ssion'

Like '-**tion**' and '-**sion**', '-**ssion**' makes the /shun/ sound, e.g. pa**ssion**.

The suffix '-**ssion**' is often added to a verb to make a noun.

'-**ssion**' is added to verbs ending in '**ss**', '**mit**', '**ede**' and '**ede**'.

- If the verb ends in '**ss**', only add '-**ion**',
  e.g. to expre**ss** → expre**ssion**.
- If the verb ends in '**mit**', remove the '**t**' before adding '-**ssion**',
  e.g. to ad**mit** → admi**ssion**.
- If the verb ends in '**ede**' or '**eed**', remove the last two letters before adding '-**ssion**',
  e.g. to succ**eed** → succe**ssion**.

A Complete these words using '-tion', '-sion' or '-ssion'. Use the rules explained above and on pages 40 and 52, or a dictionary.

percu	ques	colli	mi	man
aggre	direc	admi	pen	infec

B Complete the table with '-ssion' words and their root verbs.

'-ssion'	Root Verb	'-ssion'	Root Verb
submission			to impress
	to succeed	discussion	
progression			to permit
	to obsess	concession	

C Correct the misspelled words. Cross out the word that doesn't belong.

1. Alejandro has a (pashun) _____ for (transmition) _____ music.

2. 'It's raining cats and dogs!' is an (expretion) _____
   that means it is (profesion) _____ raining heavily.

3. The lawyer was unable to get a (confesion) _____
   from the (possechun) _____ criminal.

Grammar – Speech Marks

Speech marks (" ") are placed before and after **direct speech** to show exactly what a person has said. The punctuation (comma, full stop, exclamation mark or question mark) is always placed inside the speech marks.

Examples: Keith asked Lauren, "What time is it?"

"I won the race!" shouted Maura.

"Today is Monday," explained Olga, "so I am going swimming."

A In your copy, rewrite these with the correct punctuation to show direct speech.

1. May I go to the bathroom please asked Lorna

2. Helga's teacher told her you must have your project ready by tomorrow

3. What would you like for dinner asked Dad there's pizza or pasta

4. Where are you going asked Fred I'm just going to the library replied Tim

Indirect speech is when words spoken are described by another person. Indirect speech does not need speech marks.

Direct speech example: "Can I have an ice-cream, please?" asked Timmy.
Indirect speech example: Timmy asked if he could have an ice-cream.

B In your copy, rewrite these as indirect speech.

1. "I'll be back later," called Ferdia to Cathal.

2. "Do you know what time it is?" asked Valerie.

3. "I think I broke my arm when I fell out of the tree!" cried Ethan.

4. Gillian said to Clíona, "I love your dress."

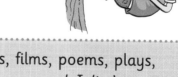

Single speech marks are also used to show the titles of books, films, poems, plays, songs and albums, e.g. William Shakespeare wrote the play, 'Romeo and Juliet'.

C Rewrite these with the correct use of speech marks.

1. Louis Sachar wrote the novel, *Holes*.

2. Ed Sheeran wrote the song, Lego House, which is on his first album, *Plus*.

3. I went to the cinema see *Ice Age* for my birthday.

D Dictation: Listen to your teacher and write the sentences in your copy.

I can do this!   I'm getting there.   I need help!

Oral Language

A Fortunately/unfortunately

Sit in a circle as a group or class. The first person must begin a story with one sentence. The second person adds a sentence beginning with 'unfortunately'. The third person adds a sentence beginning with 'fortunately'. Continue around the circle, changing the story with fortunately/unfortunately.

Example: On his twelfth birthday, Kevin discovered that he had super powers.

Unfortunately, he could only use them when it was raining.

Fortunately, he lived in Ireland, where it rains a lot.

Writing Genre – Narrative Writing

The **language of a narrative** should include:

- nouns and pronouns that refer to specific characters, e.g. they, he, Stanley.
- first or third person; I, we or he, they, she.
- past tense, e.g. wandered, thought.
- action verbs, e.g. pounced, stumbled.
- descriptive adjectives, e.g. enchanting, terrifying, picturesque.
- linking words to show time, e.g. meanwhile, after that, later on.
- dialogue using direct speech, e.g. "You should have run when you had the chance!" cackled the evil witch.

> **Top tip!**
>
> Remember to move onto the next line for each new person speaking so that your narrative is easy to read.

A Review, edit and rewrite your magical narrative story.

1. Make sure that your narrative has all of the following:
   - Setting
   - Series of two events – an initiating event and a problem
   - Resolution
   - Narrative language

2. Read over your narrative and edit it for spelling, punctuation and grammar.

3. Rewrite your narrative and include:
   - An illustration
   - An interesting title

4. Check your work using the narrative self-assessment checklist.

B Drama: Conscience Alley

The class stands in two lines, creating a Conscience Alley. In the role of Stanley, a pupil walks through Conscience Alley, listening to advice from the other pupils about what he should do next. Once he reaches the end, Stanley must decide what to do. The class then breaks into groups of four or five to act out his choice.

Comprehension Strategies

A Before reading: Questioning chart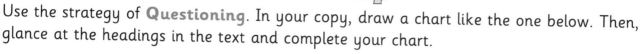

Use the strategy of **Questioning**. In your copy, draw a chart like the one below. Then, glance at the headings in the text and complete your chart.

Question	Why did I think of this question?	What is answered?	Answer	How can I get the answer?
What is the population?				By looking the answer up on Google.

B During reading: Wow word wall

Use the strategy of **Word Attack**. (Do you remember how to attack words? Look back to page vi.) Record your tricky words as you read and make a 'Wow word wall' as a class.

C During reading: Turn on the lights!

Use the strategy of **Synthesising**. Stop and notice when something in the text is clarified or explained. This is known as a 'lightbulb moment'. Record your lightbulb moments below.

D After reading: Main point

Use the strategy of **Determining Importance**. Decide on what you think is the main point in each paragraph. In groups, decide on a group main point. You must justify why you think yours is the main point.

E After reading: My place

Use the strategy of **Inferring**. In pairs, using evidence from the text, describe to your partner what life is like in Nepal.

Comprehension

STOP! Use your dictionary to find out the meaning of the **bold** words below.

Nepal

Nepal, one of the poorest countries in the world, has **stunning** natural features and a complicated political background.

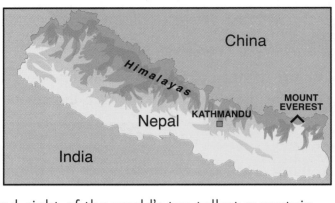

Geography

Nepal is **located** in South Asia between China and India. It is home to the Himalayas and eight of the world's ten tallest mountain peaks, including Mount Everest, the tallest mountain in the world at 8,850 metres. Its capital city is Kathmandu. Most of its people live in the hilly region of the Kathmandu Valley and the **fertile** southern **plain** of the Terai. The **climate** varies from cold summers and harsh winters in the mountainous region in the north to **subtropical** summers and mild winters in the lowlands of the south.

History

Now a **democracy**, Nepal was once a **monarchy**, ruled by the Shah family since 1769. In 1996, **rebels** began to protest the monarch-led government. This led to a ten-year civil war until 2006, when the government signed a peace agreement with the rebels. In 2008, the newly elected government voted for a democratic republic. Nepal is now ruled by a prime minister with a presidential **figurehead**, much like Ireland.

Nepal is the only country in the world not to have a rectangular or square flag.

People and culture

Nepal's most common religion is Hinduism, but many people also practise Buddhism. Buddhism is believed to have been **founded** in Nepal by a prince named Siddartha Guatama; the Buddha. The caste system, although illegal now, is still in use in Nepal. In this system, people are treated differently depending on the social group into which they are born. The four main castes are: Hindus from India; Bhotes from Tibet, who live in the mountains; hill tribes, including the Sherpas who act as guides for mountain climbers, and Newars, the **indigenous** people living in the Kathmandu Valley.

Nature

Nepal is home to interesting animals such as the Bengal tiger and the snow leopard, which are **endangered** due to **deforestation**. The Nepalese people use wood for energy, but the landscape becomes **fragile** and **erodes** when trees are cut down.

Its remarkable natural features, **turbulent** history and fascinating culture make Nepal a truly unique country.

A In your copy, go investigate. 🔍

1. In what year did the government and the rebels sign a peace agreement?
2. Name the two countries that border Nepal.
3. How many of the world's ten tallest mountains are not located in Nepal?
4. What is the main religion in Nepal?
5. Explain the term 'caste system'.
6. Why are the animals mentioned in the text endangered?

B In your copy, give your opinion. 💭

1. Why do you think the rebels fought for a new government?
2. Would you prefer the job of the prime minister or the president? Explain.
3. Explain why many people in Nepal might live in the southern plain of the Terai.
4. The name 'Everest' means 'the Forehead of the Sky'. Why do you think this is?
5. Do you agree with the caste system in Nepal? Explain your answer.
6. Would you like to visit Nepal? Why/Why not?

C Vocabulary ✏️

1. Search the text to find the antonym (opposite) of each word.

   (a) shortest: _____
   (b) excluding: _____
   (c) boring: _____
   (d) sturdy: _____
   (e) highlands: _____

2. Compound words are formed using two different words. Join these words together to make compound words.

   (a) back   tropical   _____
   (b) book   lands   _____
   (c) figure   head   _____
   (d) sub   case   _____
   (e) high   ground   background

D Cloze procedure: 'The Story of Buddha'. Fill in the blanks. ✏️

_____ was founded over two thousand _____ ago. Siddartha Gautama was a wealthy prince whose father _____ to protect him. The first time Siddartha left the palace grounds, he was horrified to see suffering, sickness _____ death. He also saw a monk living a calm and plain life and took this as a _____ that he should do the same in order to end human suffering. Siddartha _____ the world, studying with religious men, but found no answers. He retreated to a life of solitude. _____ day, while sitting under a tree in meditation, _____ found Nirvana and the way to end human _____. From then on he was _____ as Buddha, 'the Enlightened One'.

63

Phonics – '-ation'

'**-ation**' is a suffix that can be added to verbs to make nouns.

Examples: operate → oper**ation**   locate → loc**ation**

The '**a**' makes the long /a/ sound and '**tion**' is pronounced /**chun**/.

A Write the root verb for each '-ation' noun.

1. abbreviation _____
2. dictation _____
3. meditation _____
4. disqualification _____
5. magnification _____
6. emigration _____
7. extermination _____
8. hibernation _____
9. education _____
10. information _____
11. creation _____
12. vacation _____
13. justification _____
14. levitation _____
15. association _____
16. conversation _____
17. investigation _____
18. simulation _____
19. decoration _____
20. interrogation _____

B In your copy, pick some of the '-ation' words above and write their meaning. Choose a number to challenge yourself. Use a dictionary to help you.

C Complete these by changing each root verb to an '-ation' noun.

| cancel | recommend | celebrate | vibrate | illustrate | translate | pronounce |

1. Ivan is reading the Russian _____ of his favourite book.

2. "There has been a _____, so we can fit you in tomorrow," said the hostess over the telephone.

3. Quentin Blake drew beautiful _____ for Roald Dahl's books.

4. "Please turn off your mobile," cried the professor. "The _____ is a distraction to the other students."

5. I am learning a new language and find the _____ of some words difficult.

6. Olivia watched 'Monsters, Inc.' on Agné's _____.

7. There will be a big (celebrate) _____ for my brother's wedding.

Grammar – the Apostrophe

The **apostrophe** is used to show that letters have been removed from shortened words. These are called contractions.

Examples: cannot → can't   he is → he's

A Rewrite these words as contractions.

1. do not _____
3. she had _____
5. will not _____
7. could have _____
9. it is _____

2. they are _____
4. we will _____
6. you are _____
8. I am _____
10. I would _____

Top tip!

It's = it is.

It's very cold today.

Its = ownership.

The cat licks its paw.

The **apostrophe** can also be used to show ownership.

For a single owner, we add '**s**' to the end of the word, e.g. The girl'**s** doll.

For a single owner ending in '**s**', the rule is the same, e.g. James'**s** house.

B Rewrite these with apostrophes.

1. The bag belonging to the man   the man's bag
2. The cake belonging to Lisa
3. The bike belonging to Louis
4. The cat belonging to the girl
5. The pencil belonging to Tess

C In your copy, rewrite these using apostrophes correctly.

1. I cant go to Sarahs party, because Im sick.
2. The boys hand isnt broken, its just bruised.
3. The bird feeds its chicks.
4. Well be late for school if we dont hurry.
5. Jennifer likes to visit Mollys, Bens and Elaines houses.
6. The dog buried its bones outside and now it cant find them.
7. "You shouldve returned Carloss book yesterday," said Mum.

Top tip!

Be careful! Not all of these need apostrophes.

D Dictation: Listen to your teacher and write the sentences in your copy.

I can do this!   I'm getting there.   I need help!

Oral Language

A What's the country?

Pair work: Pupil A thinks of a country. Pupil B then asks questions to try to discover the name of the country. Swap roles once you have guessed your partner's country. Use these questions or make up your own:

- What continent is it on?
- What does its flag look like?
- What are some of its big cities?
- What kinds of food are eaten there?
- What might a tourist do there?

Remember to pick a country you know a lot about so that you can answer the questions.

Writing Genre – Report Writing

The purpose of **report writing** is to present factual information to the reader.

Structure:

- **Classification** (introduction) – A definition or a short description.
- **Description** – A detailed description of the topic using sub-headings.
- **Summarising comment** (conclusion) – A summary of the topic or an impersonal comment evaluating the topic.
- **Other** – A labelled diagram, a fact box (interesting information that doesn't fit into your sub-headings) or a glossary (a dictionary with subject-specific vocabulary).

A Plan, organise and write a report on a country of your choice (except Ireland).

1. Research your country using the internet, books or an atlas. Use your research to complete a mind map for your chosen country like the one below. Look back over the report on page 62 for ideas on what may be included in each section.

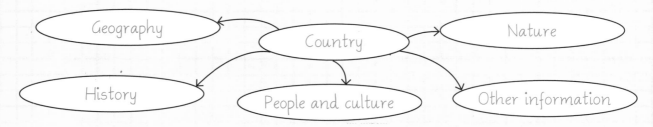

2. Using the information in your mind map, write the first draft of your report in your own words. Remember to include interesting information to keep your reader informed and entertained.

B Debate: Imagine that you are meeting with the leaders of Nepal. Plan a speech to convince them to end deforestation.

Steve Jobs

Comprehension Strategies

A Before reading: True or false?

Use the strategy of **Predicting**. Write five statements about Steve Jobs below. Check to see if you were right after reading.

1. Steve Jobs owns Apple.
2. Steve Jobs is a billionaire.
3. Steve Jobs was born in 1955.
4. Steve Jobs passed away 7 years ago.
5. _____

B During reading: Just like …

Use the strategy of **Making Connections**. As you read, record some of Steve Jobs's character traits. Make connections to yourself, the outside world and other texts. Explain how each character trait relates to you, someone you know or a fictional character.

Character trait	Just like me:	Like someone I know:	Reminds me of… from…

C After reading: Interview

Use the strategy of **Inferring**. In your copy, make a list of interview questions that you would ask Steve Jobs if he were still alive. In pairs, try to answer each other's questions accurately using evidence from the text.

D After reading: Main-idea pyramid

Use the strategies of **Determining Importance** and **Summarising**. As a class, brainstorm the main points of the text on post-it notes. Group these points into categories and place them at the bottom of a pyramid. Combine the grouped points into one point on the next level of the pyramid. Keep doing this until one point remains.

Comprehension

STOP! Use your dictionary to find out the meaning of the **bold** words below.

Steve Jobs

Steve Jobs was an American **entrepreneur** and inventor, best known for **co-founding** Apple Computers.

He was born on February 24th 1955 in San Francisco, California. He was adopted by Paul and Clara Jobs. At the age of five, Steve and his family moved to Mountain View, California. While he was growing up, he loved to work with and learn about electronics with his father. He often got into trouble in school for playing pranks. He was a clever student, but was bored easily. After high school, he **attended** Reed College in Oregon, but again, became bored in class and left college to take a job at Atari, a video-game maker.

When he was twenty-one years old, he **reconnected** with Steve Wozniak, an old friend who was also interested in electronics. Wozniak invented his own personal computer. Before this, it was not common for people to have computers in their homes. Jobs was so **impressed** that he **suggested** they start their own company. They **formed** the company,

Apple Computers Inc, in 1976 and began making computers in Jobs's garage. They named their first computer the Apple I. The company became **successful** when Wozniak invented the Apple II. However, the Apple III and the Lisa were not as popular. Jobs then **developed** the Macintosh, which was much more expensive than **similar** products such as the PC and, so, not as popular. Taking the blame for the drop in sales, Jobs resigned from Apple in 1985.

Steve Jobs with the Apple I

He did not give up. He founded NeXT Inc. and began **producing** high-end personal computers. However, they were too expensive for most people and Jobs began losing money again until he decided to turn NeXT Inc. into a software company. In 1986, he bought a **graphics** company and changed its name to Pixar. In 1991, the company was asked by Disney to make 'Toy Story', the first-ever computer-**animated** film. Pixar is now an **extremely** successful company, having made films that include 'Finding Nemo', 'Monsters, Inc.', 'Up' and 'Brave', which was dedicated to Jobs.

In 1997, Apple bought NeXT Inc. Jobs returned to Apple as CEO (chief executive officer) and began designing more products to save the **struggling** company. Apple became known as a **revolutionary** electronics company, producing the iPod, iTunes and, in 2007, the iPhone, which was the first mobile phone of its kind.

Steve Jobs died on October 5th 2011 from pancreatic cancer. He is **considered** by many to have been one of the greatest entrepreneurs of his time.

A In your copy, go investigate.

1. In what year did Steve Jobs and his family move to Mountain View?
2. Why did Steve Jobs get into trouble in school?
3. What caused Apple to become successful?
4. Why did Steve Jobs decide to turn NeXT Inc. into a software company?
5. In what year did Pixar begin to make the first-ever computer-animated film?
6. Why has Apple become known as a revolutionary electronics company?

B In your copy, give your opinion.

1. Where do you think Steve Jobs got his love of electronics?
2. Why do you think Steve Jobs was impressed with Steve Wozniak?
3. Do you think Steve Jobs did the right thing by resigning from Apple in 1985?
4. Why do you think Steve Jobs decided to name his new company NeXT Inc?
5. 'Brave' was released in 2012. Why do you think it was dedicated to Steve Jobs?
6. In your opinion, what was Steve Jobs's greatest achievement?

C Vocabulary

1. In your copy, choose five bold words from the text and write a sentence for each.
2. Correct the spelling of the words below from the text.

   (a) elictroniks _____   (b) sucsesful _____

   (c) gratest _____   (d) desining _____

   (e) envented _____   (f) extremley _____

   (g) nown _____   (h) entrepenure _____

   (i) cheif _____   (j) softwear _____

D Cloze procedure: 'The Computer'. Fill in the blanks.

A computer is _____ electronic device that processes information. A _____
works by taking in information or data (input), storing it until it is ready to figure it
_____ (memory), working on it to solve the problem (processing) and giving the answer
(output). These machines have _____ a lot since they were first invented. The first
_____ could only perform one or _____ functions. They filled entire rooms,
cost millions to _____ and were only used by governments _____ big companies.
These _____, faster, more powerful computers can fit in your pocket. Computers are found
everywhere in the _____ around us, from mobile phones to microwaves.

Phonics – '-ify'

'-**ify**' can be used to change nouns and adjectives into verbs,
e.g. horror → horr**ify**.

A Complete the table of verbs and root nouns or adjectives. Underline
the nouns and ring the adjectives.

Root	Verb	Root	Verb
diverse	diversify	identity	
class			personify
	simplify	beauty	
solid			falsify
	specify	sign	
justice			intensify
	terrify	false	
dignity			electrify
	clarify	pure	

B In your copy, choose a number of the '-ify' words above and write a
sentence for each. Choose a number to challenge yourself.

C Choose the correct word to complete each sentence.

| terrify | magnify | mystify | clarify | dignify | disqualify | purify | testify |

1. "We must ⬚⬚⬚⬚⬚⬚ this water before we drink it," agreed the campers.
2. "I am not going to ⬚⬚⬚⬚⬚⬚ that with an answer," sniffed the angry woman.
3. I didn't understand the question. Could you please ⬚⬚⬚⬚⬚⬚
   what you meant?
4. Doctors need to ⬚⬚⬚⬚⬚⬚ the blood samples that they
   test in order to figure out what is wrong with the patient.
5. The haunted house will ⬚⬚⬚⬚⬚⬚ the young boys and girls.
6. Alan witnessed a robbery, so now he must ⬚⬚⬚⬚⬚⬚ in court.
7. "Cheating will ⬚⬚⬚⬚⬚⬚ you from this competition,"
   announced the judges.
8. "I will ⬚⬚⬚⬚⬚⬚ and amaze you!" exclaimed the magician before the show.

Grammar – Prepositions

A preposition relates a noun or a pronoun to another word in a sentence. It often refers to the position of the noun or pronoun.

Examples: My bag is **under** the (table).

I jumped **into** the (pool).

A Underline the preposition and ring the noun or pronoun to which it relates in each sentence.

1. We always park our car behind the house.
2. Emily sits beside the window in school.
3. Mrs Black placed the cake on the kitchen counter.
4. Prija lives in India.
5. I walk through the town on my way to school.
6. Irene likes shopping with her mother.
7. There will be a famous author at the bookshop tomorrow.
8. We flew over France on our way to Italy.
9. I bought a present for my sister's birthday.
10. My shoes are beneath the pile of clothes in my room.

B Certain prepositions are used with specific verbs. Write suitable prepositions for each verb below. In your copy, choose one preposition for each verb and write a sentence using the pair.

under   on   beside   about   with   near   at   to   through   behind   in   for   around

1. live	with, near, behind, in…	2. put	
3. move		4. swim	
5. sit		6. play	
7. walk		8. fight	
9. talk		10. work	

C Dictation: Listen to your teacher and write the sentences in your copy.

 I can do this!   I'm getting there.   I need help!

Oral Language

A Vocabulary game

Reports should always contain text-specific vocabulary.

In pairs, play this game to extend your vocabulary. For each of the categories, create a list of words. Take it in turns to name something you would associate with each word. A player wins when the other cannot think of a new word. Words cannot be repeated.

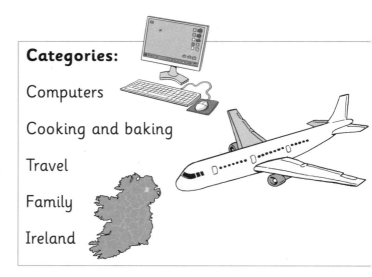

Categories:

Computers

Cooking and baking

Travel

Family

Ireland

Writing Genre – Report Writing

The **language of a report** should include:

- general subjects, e.g. the people of Nepal, the computer, they, it.
- impersonal objective language. First-person pronouns (I, my, etc.) and opinions are **not** included.
- timeless present tense, e.g. are, have, is, belongs, protects.
- subject-specific vocabulary, e.g. subtropical, megabyte, habitat.
- factual, clear adjectives, e.g. harsh winters, religious people.

A Review, edit and rewrite your country report.

1. Make sure that your report has all of the following:
   - Classification (introduction)
   - A detailed description of all of the sub-headings from your mind map
   - A summarising comment
   - Report-specific language

2. Read over your report and edit it for spelling, punctuation, grammar and relevant information.

3. Rewrite your narrative and include:
   - A labelled map
   - A fact box

4. Check your work using the report self-assessment checklist.

B Art activity

Using a variety of different materials – pencil, chalk, paint, paper, crêpe paper, etc. – create the flag of your chosen country to display alongside your report.

Anne Frank: the Diary of a Young Girl

13

Comprehension Strategies

A Before reading: Changing images

Use the strategy of **Visualising**. Draw an image to show what you can picture …

Before reading	During reading	After reading

B During reading: This reminds me of …

Use the strategy of **Making Connections**. As you read, mark places in the text where you make connections about:

- yourself – This reminds me of a time I …
- another text – This reminds me of something I read …
- the outside world – This reminds me of what I know about …

C During reading: I think that … because …

Use the strategy of **Inferring**. As you read, stop along the way to make inferences with evidence from the text.

- Reading between the lines, I think that … because …
- I think the character is thinking … because …
- I think the character will … because …
- I think this happened a long time ago, because …
- I think … will happen, because …

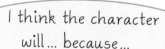

I think the character will … because…

D After reading: Beat the buzzer.

Use the strategy of **Questioning** and the skill of **Skimming**. Write a question about the text on a post-it. Your teacher can collect all of the questions and ask them of the class one by one. You must then skim the text to locate the exact line that gives the answer. When you have found it, press the buzzer (i.e. call out your name) to answer.

Comprehension

 Use your dictionary to find out the meaning of the **bold** words below.

Anne Frank; the Diary of a Young Girl

Anne Frank was an ordinary young **Jewish** girl living in Amsterdam when the **persecution** of the Jewish people during World War II forced her family into hiding. Anne's only **solace** during this time was to record her life in the **annex** in her beloved diary, Kitty.

Anne Frank

Wednesday, 8 July 1942

Dearest Kitty,

Margot and I started packing our most important **belongings** into a **satchel**. The first thing I stuck in was this diary, and then curlers, handkerchiefs, schoolbooks, a comb and some old letters. **Preoccupied** by the thought of going into hiding, I stuck the craziest things in the satchel, but I'm not sorry. Memories mean more to me than dresses…

Miep arrived and promised to return later that night, taking with her a bag full of shoes, dresses, jackets, underwear and stockings. After that it was quiet in our flat; none of us felt like eating. It was still hot, and everything was very strange…

Miep and Jan Gies came at eleven. Miep, who's worked for Father's company since 1933, has become a close friend, and so has her husband, Jan. Once again, shoes, stockings, books and underwear disappeared into Miep's bag and Jan's deep pockets. At eleven-thirty they too disappeared.

I was exhausted, and even though I knew it'd be my last night in my own bed, I fell asleep right away and didn't wake up until Mother called me at five-thirty the next morning. Fortunately, it wasn't as hot as Sunday; a warm rain fell throughout the day. The four of us were wrapped in so many layers of clothes it looked as if we were going off to spend the night in a refrigerator, and all that just so we could take more clothes with us. No Jew in our situation would dare leave the house with a suitcase full of clothes. I was wearing two vests, three pairs of pants, a dress, and over that a skirt, a jacket, a raincoat, two pairs of stockings, heavy shoes, a cap, a scarf and lots more. I was suffocating even before we left the house, but no one bothered to ask me how I felt.

Margot stuffed her satchel with schoolbooks, went to get her bicycle and, with Miep leading the way, rode off into the great unknown. At any rate, that's how I thought of it, since I still didn't know where our hiding place was.

At seven-thirty we too closed the door behind us… The stripped beds, the breakfast things on the table, the pound of meat for the cat in the kitchen – all of these created the **impression** that we'd left in a hurry. But we weren't interested in impressions. We just wanted to get out of there, to get away and reach our **destination** in safety. Nothing else mattered.

More tomorrow.

Yours, Anne

A In your copy, go investigate.

1. Why were Anne and her family forced to go into hiding?
2. On what day was this diary entry written?
3. How did Miep know Anne's family?
4. Why were Anne and her family wearing so many items of clothing?
5. How did Anne feel as a result of wearing so many items of clothing?
6. What gave the impression that Anne's family had left in a hurry?

B In your copy, give your opinion.

1. What kinds of things are important to Anne? How do you know this?
2. What would you have packed if you were Anne?
3. Why do you think Anne says, "No Jew in our situation would dare leave the house with a suitcase full of clothes"?
4. Why do you think Anne felt that Margot was riding into "the great unknown"?
5. Do you think Anne and her family reached their destination? Why/Why not?
6. How would you have felt if you were Anne? Explain.

C Vocabulary

1. Break into groups and search recount texts, including this one, for words that demonstrate the following types of recount language: who, where, when, what, why and how.
2. Each group can then use the list they have created to make a poster of the language that they found. Include a title and a simple picture or symbol.
3. Add to this poster throughout the week when you come across any language that you think may help with recount writing.

D Cloze procedure: 'Who was Anne Frank?' Fill in the blanks.

Anne Frank was a German-born Jewish girl _____ lived in Amsterdam during World War II. In order to _____ persecution by the Nazis, the Frank family, along with four other people, hid in a secret annex above Otto Frank's office in Amsterdam. Anne and her _____ spent two years in hiding from the horrors of _____ Holocaust. While there, Anne wrote in her diary, _____. She chronicled their _____ in the attic, vividly describing the fear, hunger and frustration of living in such confined quarters for such a long period of _____. Anne was fifteen when her hiding place was _____ by the Nazis. She was sent to a concentration camp in Germany, where _____ died of typhus. Her _____ is one of the most powerful stories to emerge from the Holocaust.

Phonics – '-ough'

'-**ough**' makes many different sounds: **/uff/ /off/ /aw/ /oa/ /oo/ /ow/**
Examples:

although	rough	bough	though	trough	sought
thought	thorough	cough	enough	thoughtful	doughnut
bought	plough	brought	tough	fought	borough
drought	through	dough	breakthrough		

A Write each word above into the correct column according to its sound. Use your dictionary if you're not sure of the words.

/aw/	/oo/	/uff/	/ow/	/oo/	/off/

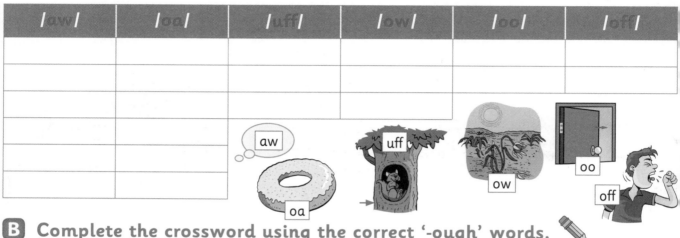

B Complete the crossword using the correct '-ough' words.

Across

1. To enter by one end or side and exit by the other

2. Past tense of 'to seek', meaning to look for

4. A large, main branch of a tree

5. Sufficient amount for the want or need

Down

1. A container used to hold food or water for animals

3. Extremely attentive to detail

C Fix the spelling of each '-ough' word and cross out the one that doesn't make sense.

1. I (brawt) _____ a present to my cousin's birthday (ruff) _____ party.

2. My (tuff) _____ grandad has a (plow) _____ on his farm.

3. Reuben had a (coff) _____ , so he could not go to (doanut) _____ training.

4. Daniella (thawtful) _____ enjoyed her walk (threw) _____ the park.

5. There (thawt) _____ is a terrible (drowt) _____ in Ethiopia.

Grammar – Verb Tenses

Verbs have three main tenses that tell us when something happens.
Past tense: It happened in the past, e.g. I **walked** home from school.
Present tense: It happens regularly, e.g. I **walk** home from school.
Future tense: It will happen in the future, e.g. I **will walk** home from school.

A Underline the verbs and tick the correct tense.

	Past	Present	Future
1. Nadia lived in Russia until she was ten years old.			
2. I will dress up for the parade on St Patrick's Day.			
3. Ostriches can run faster than horses.			
4. I ate all of my dinner so I could have my dessert.			
5. Xavier will play with his baby brother at the weekend.			

Verbs change depending on the tense.
Past tense: Add 'ed' to the ends of verbs in the past, e.g. I clean**ed**.
Present tense: Use the root verb for verbs in the present, e.g. I **clean**.
Future tense: Use '**will**' and the root for verbs in the future, e.g. I **will clean**.
Irregular verbs follow no pattern, e.g. went, go, will go.

B Fill in the tense table. It contains regular and irregular verbs.

Past	Present	Future
	drink	
painted		
		will canter
	tell	

Past	Present	Future
saw		
		will examine
	eat	
dug		

C Underline the verbs in these sentences. In your copy, rewrite the sentences in the correct tense. Only the verbs must change.

1. Ida is not allowed to drove her father's car until she is seventeen years old.
2. Our school quiz team win the national finals yesterday.
3. "Did you brought your homework to school today Brian?" asked Ms Kinsella.
4. I cook dinner for my family next week. I made spaghetti.

D Dictation: Listen to your teacher and write the sentences in your copy.

| I can do this! | I'm getting there. | I need help! |

Oral Language

A Recount stories

In pairs, use the lists of recount language that you created in the vocabulary activity on page 75 to create two recount stories. One recount should be a serious tale, using collections of words that make sense when used together in a story. The other recount should be silly, using words that don't quite belong in the same story.

Writing Genre – Recount Writing

The purpose of a **recount** is to retell or recount past experiences or events. Recounts may be personal, factual or imaginative.

Structure:

- **Setting** – Set the scene for the reader. Include who, where, when, what, why and how.
- **Events** – Told in time order.
- **Concluding statement** – Can be in the form of the author's feelings in a personal recount or an evaluative comment in a factual recount.

A Plan, organise and write a diary entry in the form of a recount.

The diary entry can belong to either a person you have studied in history or your favourite fictional character.

Example: Martin Luther King

1. Plan your recount using the plan below.

Diary entry for: _____

Setting

Who	Where	When	What	Why	How

Events

Event 1	Event 2	Event 3	Event 4

Concluding statement

2. Use the information in your plan to write the first draft of your recount.

B Drama: Act out the stories that you and your partner created in the oral language activity above.

Rebellion in the Capital 14

Comprehension Strategies

A Before reading: KWL chart

Use the strategies of **Making Connections** and **Questioning**. Use the chart below to record your background knowledge (schema) on the 1916 Easter Rising and anything that you hope to find out from reading the text. Record what you have learned after reading.

KWL Chart		
What I know	**What I want to know**	**What I have learned**

B During reading: Wow word wall

Use the strategy of **Word Attack**. (Do you remember how to attack words? Look back to page vi.) Record your tricky words as you read and make a 'Wow word wall' as a class.

C After reading: Where, who, what…

Use the strategy of **Determining Importance**. Record key words from the text that show …

The setting	The characters	The main events
Dublin City G.P.O	Páidraig Peurse, Sean Connolly, Thomas Clarke, James Connolly, Eoin Macneill	

D After reading: Debate

Use the strategy of **Synthesising**. Use evidence from the text and your schema to debate the topic, 'The 1916 Easter Rising should have been called off'.

Comprehension

STOP! Use your dictionary to find out the meaning of the **bold** words below.

DAILY TIMES

REBELLION IN THE CAPITAL

SEÁN RYAN

TUE. APRIL 25TH 1916

DUBLIN CITY LIES IN **turmoil** this morning as **insurgents** attempt to lead a rebellion against English rule in Ireland. Groups by the name of the Irish Volunteers and the Irish Citizen Army have **seized** the city in an attempt to **proclaim** Ireland a republic. Their success remains to be seen.

It appears this rising had been planned for some time, with volunteers around the country **pledging** their support for the **revolt**. However, the British **interception** of the German cargo ship, the *'Aud'*, which was bringing **ammunition** to Dublin, caused Irish Volunteer leader, MacNeill, on Easter Sunday, to send out a message to **radicals** around Ireland cancelling the rising **scheduled** for the following day. **Evidently**, two others in charge, Thomas Clarke and James Connolly, thought differently, as they ordered the attack to go ahead **regardless** of their now severely **depleted** army and **arms**.

Yesterday morning, Easter Monday, about 1,250 rebels **assembled** across Dublin City. Most **converged** at Liberty Hall, where they were given a rousing speech by James Connolly, and marched to **occupy** the following **prominent** buildings in Dublin City: Jacob's Biscuit Factory, the Four Courts, the South Dublin Union, Boland's Mills and the Jameson Distillery.

The most **notable** building **seized** was the General Post Office (GPO) on Sackville Street. **Amidst** disbelief and **jeers** from on-looking Dubliners and while a new flag reading 'Irish Republic' fluttered overhead along with the **symbolic** tricolour, teacher Pádraig Pearse read out a proclamation **declaring** Ireland a republic on behalf of the 'Provisional Government'. Interestingly, the proclamation of this supposed new republic gives equal standing to men and women; "Irishmen and Irishwomen: In the name of God and of the dead generations from which she receives her old tradition of nationhood, Ireland, through us, **summons** her children to her flag and strikes for her freedom ..." read Pearse.

The GPO, Sackville Street, now held by rebels

Meanwhile, another group, led by Seán Connolly, attempted to take Dublin Castle, the British centre of **administration** in this country. It was here that the first shot of this uprising was fired and the first death occurred. An unarmed police sergeant attempted to block the group's entry and so Connolly shot him dead. Upon seeing this **altercation**, a military guard pulled the gates closed, leaving the **mutineers** with few options. Following some **hesitation** and **indecision**, the group were forced to retreat to the nearby City Hall, which they held for less than twenty-four hours. While **barricaded** inside, Abbey actor Connolly became the first leader to die.

Currently, the city is under rebel control. Barricades have been **erected** across the city, **enraging** local citizens. Transport has ground to a halt, businesses have closed and the poor of Dublin, who, some say live in the worst **slums** of Europe, have begun to **loot** the **abandoned** shops. Beggar women and barefoot children have been seen wandering around wearing fur coats and feather hats.

British troops have been called into action, with many Irish soldiers home on leave from the Great War for Easter among their ranks.

Regardless of one's political views, one can only hope this battle concludes soon, before any more destruction or casualties befall our beloved city.

A In your copy, go investigate.

1. On what day did the events in the article take place?
2. Why did Eoin MacNeill attempt to cancel the rising?
3. How many rebels took part in the capture of Dublin City?
4. What was the main building captured by the rebels during the rising?
5. Who was the first person to die in the rising?
6. Why did the rebels want to take control of Dublin Castle?

B In your copy, give your opinion. ❴?❵

1. Do you think the rebellion was ongoing when this article was written? Use evidence from the text to support your answer.
2. Why do you think the author says it is interesting that the Proclamation gives equal standing to men and women?
3. What was the local opinion of the rising in Dublin? Explain.
4. What do you think your opinion would have been if you had lived in Dublin? Why?
5. Why do you think the author calls for a quick end to the rebellion?
6. How do you think you would have felt as a volunteer in the rising?

C Vocabulary: Use the correct bold word from the text to complete the sentences.

1. The rebels _____ many _____ buildings on Easter Monday.
2. Dublin was very poor at the time and many people lived in _____.
3. The people began to _____ local shops during the week of the Rising.
4. Many thought that the rising had been cancelled, but it went ahead as _____.
5. The German boat, the 'Aud', attempted to deliver _____ to Ireland.

D Cloze procedure: 'Elizabeth O'Farrell'. Fill in the blanks.

More _____ one hundred Irish women are known to have taken _____ in the _____, many of whom were associated with Cumann na mBan (the Women's League). The women of the rising _____ as nurses, doctors, cooks and messengers and fought bravely alongside the men in the rising. Midwife Elizabeth O'Farrell was _____ of the last people to leave the GPO. _____ played an important role in the surrender of the rebels. She delivered messages between the Irish Volunteer leaders and _____ British and accompanied Padraig _____ when he surrendered to General Lowe. Elizabeth was later removed from a photograph _____ at this historic moment. She _____ in 1957 and was buried at Glasnevin Cemetery.

Phonics – Homonyms

Homographs are words that are spelled the same, but have different meanings. When homographs sound the same, they are called **homonyms**.

Examples: swallow
– a bird
– to consume food

A Name the homonyms described below.

1. The opposite of the truth To be horizontal on a bed or the ground	
2. To have the correct answer Something that is good, proper or just	
3. An item of jewellery worn on the finger The act of calling a person on the telephone	
4. A number of items or people arranged in a straight line To propel a boat with the use of oars	
5. The currency of England A measurement of weight in the imperial system	
6. The bottom of a shoe or foot A European flat fish	

B Write both meanings for the homonyms listed below. Swap with a partner and match the homonyms to their definitions.

train	watch	organ	park	fair

1. _____   1. _____

2. _____   2. _____

3. _____   3. _____

4. _____   4. _____

5. _____   5. _____

C In your copy, for each pair of homonyms above, write a sentence that contains both meanings.

Grammar – Conjunctions

Conjunctions are words that are used to join words, phrases or parts of a sentence together. They can help make sentences more interesting, e.g.
I don't like to swim, **however** I do enjoy the beach.

Sometimes conjunctions work together, e.g.
On Friday, I set my alarm ten minutes early **in order to** be on time for my tests.

A Underline the conjunction/s in these sentences.

1. Akio walks his neighbour's dog at the weekend, even though he's afraid of dogs.
2. Georgia neither cooks nor cleans since her mother cut off her allowance.
3. My brother likes to listen to music while he does his homework.
4. "I will let you know the results of your tests once I have corrected them," explained the teacher.
5. Vid washes up while his dinner is cooking, so that he can relax after eating.
6. My mum will bring me to the cinema provided that I get all of my homework done.

Conjunctions have different functions.
'And' connects similar words or sentences, e.g. I had beans **and** toast for lunch.
'But' joins two opposite ideas, e.g. Bruno doesn't like animals, **but** he has a goldfish.
'Because' shows reason, e.g. I am not going outside, **because** it is raining.
'So' shows result, e.g. Reem studied very hard, **so** she passed the test.
'Or' shows choice, e.g. Would you like a biscuit **or** would you prefer some cake?
'If' shows condition, e.g. I'll be very sad **if** you spoil the ending of the book for me.

B Use the conjunctions above to complete these.

1. I would share my lunch with you,   I am very hungry.
2. Kate was early for the meeting,   she read her book while she waited.
3. You must brush your teeth twice a day,   you will need fillings.
4. Ursula ran home from school,   it was raining.
5. Will would be a great student   he worked a little harder.
6. Tomorrow I will tidy my room   wash up after dinner.

C In your copy, write a sentence using each of the conjunctions above correctly.

D Dictation: Listen to your teacher and write the sentences in your copy.

I can do this!   I'm getting there.   I need help!

Oral Language

A Story building

Tell a story as a group. Pupil A begins the story with one sentence. Pupil B then adds a sentence, using a linking time word with their sentence. Each pupil adds their own event until the group has a story of about ten sentences.

Add to the list of linking time words before you start.

Linking time words:
- After that
- While
- Firstly
- Next
-
-
-
-
-

Example:

Once there was a princess who was bored of princess things, until one day, she met a strange woman who said she could help her. Meanwhile, the king was planning the princess's arranged marriage.

Writing Genre – Recount Writing

The **language of a recount** should include:
- first or third person, e.g. I, we, he, they.
- simple past tense, e.g. raced, spoke.
- mostly action verbs, e.g. saved, argued, discovered.
- linking time words, e.g. initially, eventually, after that, meanwhile.
- words and phrases to show time and place, e.g. last weekend, over the Himalayas.

A Review, edit and rewrite your diary entry recount.

1. Make sure that your recount has all of the following:
   - Setting
   - Four sequential events
   - A concluding statement
   - Recount language

2. Read over your recount and edit it for spelling, punctuation and grammar.

3. Rewrite your recount and try to:
   - stop along the way to describe people or places in more detail.
   - entertain and inform your reader.

4. Check your work using the recount self-assessment checklist.

Top tip!

Think about the time and location of events. Use a lot of phrases to describe the action taking place.

B Art activity

Design a diary cover for the person you have chosen to write about. Think carefully about their age, gender, personality, interests and the time in which they live.

Comprehension Strategies

A **Before reading: Picture flick**

Use the strategy of **Predicting**. Cover the text and look only at the images. Predict what this poem will be about based on the images.

B **During reading: Five senses**

Use the strategy of **Visualising**. As you read, record what you can see, hear, smell, taste and touch.

C **After reading: Fact or fib?**

Use the strategy of **Synthesising**. Write three facts and one fib about the text. Then, in pairs, swap your lists and find each other's fib.

Facts

1. _____

_____

2. _____

_____

3. _____

_____

4. _____

_____

D **After reading: Crystal ball**

Use the strategy of **Predicting**. Use your crystal ball to predict what will happen next.

I predict that…   I imagine that…   I wonder if…   I think that…

I think that… will happen, because…   Maybe… will happen, because…

Comprehension

 STOP! Use your dictionary to find out the meaning of the **bold** words below.

The Sound Collector

A stranger called this morning
Dressed all in black and grey
Put every sound into a bag
And carried them away

The whistling of the kettle
The turning of the lock
The purring of the kitten
The ticking of the clock

The popping of the toaster
The crunching of the flakes
When you spread the **marmalade**
The scraping noise it makes

The hissing of the frying pan
The ticking of the **grill**
The bubbling of the bathtub
As it starts to fill

The drumming of the raindrops
On the windowpane
When you do the washing-up
The gurgle of the drain

The crying of the baby
The squeaking of the chair
The **swishing** of the curtain
The creaking of the stair

A stranger called this morning
He didn't leave his name
Left us only silence
Life will never be the same

By Roger McGough

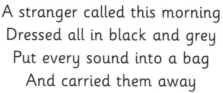

A In your copy, go investigate. 🔍

1. Who called this morning?
2. What noise does spreading the marmalade make?
3. What did the stranger leave behind him?
4. Does the poet have a pet?
5. If the poet hadn't told you it was morning, how would you have known that it was?
6. Can you find any rhyming words in the poem? Is there a pattern?

B In your copy, give your opinion. 💭

1. Why do you think the stranger was 'dressed all in black and grey'?
2. What kind of place did the stranger visit? How do you know?
3. What noises can be heard in your home in the morning?
4. Why do you think the stranger didn't leave his name?
5. Why will life 'never be the same'?
6. How would you feel if someone took all of the sounds out of the world?

Onomatopoeia (on-o-mat-o-pay-a) is when a word sounds like the noise that it is describing, e.g. buzz.

C Vocabulary: List the onomatopoeic words that you can find in the poem and add to the list with words of your own. ✏️

D Cloze procedure: 'Strange News'. Fill in the blanks. ✏️

The news reporter couldn't _____ what he was reading. People would laugh ____ him for reporting on this story, but he had a _____ to do and the producer was waving her arms in the _____, urging him to get on with it, as they were _____ on air.

'This just in, folks. There have been reports of a man dressed in black and _____ entering homes in the local area and stealing the _____. One family have stated that their clock has stopped _____, they cannot hear the rain on the _____ and there is no sound when the _____ cries, although they say that the _____ can keep that last sound. Gardaí are urging anyone with _____ to come forward. More on this strange story after the _____."

Phonics – Rhyming Words

Rhyme occurs when then the endings of words sound the same. Rhyming words do not necessarily have the same spelling.

Examples: cat – sat   foot – put

A Complete the crossword. The answer to each clue rhymes with the word written in brackets.

Across

2. A sound made when sad or frustrated (buy)
4. To make a musical sound with your mouth (come)
6. Not smooth (stuff)
7. Part of a plant (power)
9. Top part of the body (said)
10. To move about on hands and knees (fall)

Down

1. A number (plate)
3. A farm animal similar to a duck (loose)
5. An animal similar to a donkey (pool)
8. Not a door (throw)

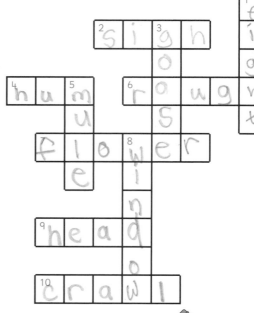

Crossword answers filled in: 2 across sigh, 1 down eight, 3 down goose, 4 across hum, 5 down mule, 6 across rough, 7 across flower, 8 down window, 9 across head, 10 across crawl

B Ring the correct rhyming words to complete each sentence.

1. I water the **plants / aunts** every day so that they will **show / grow**.
2. Jupiter is the largest **granite / planet** in the **Solar / roller** System.
3. Karolina loves to **read / knead** and **saint / paint** to relax after school.
4. "Could you please **class / pass** the **shed / bread**?" asked Rachel during dinner.
5. Tigers are the largest **members / embers** of the **bat / cat** family.
6. I would like to go for a **hawk / walk**. Have you seen my **coat / goat**?
7. Paul likes to **bite / write** songs and **play / neigh** them for his family.
8. Mrs Fitzgerald **cook / took** her children to the **beach / speech** on Saturday.
9. May I borrow your **jeweller / ruler**? I **lost / tossed** mine.
10. The 'Mona Lisa' is also **blown / known** as 'La Gioconda'. It was painted **by / eye** Leonardo da Vinci.

C In your copy, use pairs of rhyming words above (or choose your own) to write a sentence containing both words. Pick a number to challenge yourself.

Grammar – Idioms and Proverbs

An **idiom** is a phrase that has a different literal (actual) meaning to how it sounds, e.g. it's raining cats and dogs – it is raining heavily.

A Complete each idiom and write its literal meaning in your copy.

1. Pull up your ▪	▪ blue
2. Under the ▪	▪ eye
3. See eye to ▪	▪ court
4. Out of the ▪	▪ socks
5. The ball is in your ▪	▪ weather
6. Piece of ▪	▪ leg
7. Cry over spilt ▪	▪ cover
8. Costs an arm and a ▪	▪ milk
9. Judge a book by its ▪	▪ bread
10. Best thing since sliced ▪	▪ cake

B Match each expression from around the world to its literal meaning.

1. To have a stick in your ear (Danish) ▪
2. Not my circus, not my monkeys (Polish) ▪
3. To let a frog out of your mouth (Finnish) ▪
4. To have a wide face (Japanese) ▪
5. A cat's jump (German) ▪

▪ To say the wrong thing
▪ To have many friends
▪ To not listen to someone
▪ A short distance away
▪ Not my problem

A **proverb** is an old saying that gives advice or comments on everyday life, e.g. a stitch in time saves nine – doing the job now will save time and effort in the end.

C Number the boxes to match each proverb with its meaning.

1. Two wrongs don't make a right.	Words are more effective than force.
2. Don't put all of your eggs in one basket.	Revenge might make things worse.
3. Beggars can't be choosers.	Be patient.
4. Good things come to those who wait.	When asking a favour, take what you get.
5. Birds of a feather flock together.	Have a backup plan.
6. The pen is mightier than the sword.	People who spend time together are similar.

D Dictation: Listen to your teacher and write the sentences in your copy.

 I can do this!   I'm getting there.   I need help!

Oral Language

A Onomatopoeic words

As a class, make a list of the onomatopoeic sounds that you would hear at each of the following: school, the beach, a shopping centre, the zoo, a busy street, etc. Leave these lists on the board and play the games that follow.

1. **Bingo**: Draw a grid in your copy with pictures of things that would make the sounds listed. Cross off a picture when your teacher calls out the sound.

2. **Ten questions**: One pupil chooses a sound from the list. The class must guess the word by asking questions about where it might be heard or what might make this sound. The pupil can only give yes or no answers. The pupil wins if the class cannot guess after ten questions.

3. **Don't say it**: A pupil sits at the top of the room with their back to the board. The teacher points to a word on the list without them seeing. The class must describe the sound by making sounds with their mouth or body, or describing where it might be heard or what might make the sound (without saying the word).

Writing Genre – Poetry Writing

Poetry has many different **language features**, including:
- nouns and verbs that refer to specific things, events, emotions or actions.
- imaginative adjectives and adverbs, e.g. shimmering, stubbornly.
- literary devices such as rhyme, rhythm, imagery, alliteration, repetition and onomatopoeia.

A Write your own poem in the style of 'The Sound Collector'.

1. 'The Sound Collector' uses sounds from a family home in the morning. Choose a setting (e.g. a shopping centre, your school, a zoo) for your poem. Make a list of sounds that you might hear in this setting. Be specific, e.g. not 'the noise of the waves', but the 'crashing of the waves'. Try to use as many onomatopoeic words as possible. Use the class list from the oral language activity above to help you.

2. Write your own sound collector poem.
   - Use the first and last paragraphs from the original poem or challenge yourself by writing similar, but new ones.
   - Follow the pattern of the original poem, e.g. 'The _____ing of the _____'.
   - Try to use a similar rhyming pattern of ABCB (lines 2 and 4 rhyme, but lines 1 and 3 don't).
   - Change the title to describe your setting, e.g. 'The Sound Collector at the Zoo'.
   - Illustrate your poem with pictures of the scenes and sounds that it describes.

B Music: Work in small groups using percussion instruments or body percussion to create a soundtrack to 'The Sound Collector'.

Nuclear Energy: Friend or Foe?

Comprehension Strategies

A Before reading: KWL chart

Use the strategies of **Making Connections** and **Questioning**. Use the chart below to record your background knowledge (schema) on nuclear energy and anything that you hope to find out from reading the text. Record what you have learned after reading.

KWL Chart		
What I know	**What I want to know**	**What I have learned**
Nuclear energy is bad for the enviorment	What it is used for? Where do they get it? What is it made of?	There was an incident in Cherynobyl with nuclear energy where 53 people died and many more were .

B During reading: I think that … because …

Use the strategy of **Inferring**. As you read, stop along the way to make inferences with evidence from the text.

- I think that … because …
- I think this is correct, because I know that …
- Reading between the lines, I think that … because …
- I think this means … because …

> I think this means… because…

C After reading: Main-idea pyramid

Use the strategies of **Determining Importance** and **Summarising**. As a class, brainstorm the main points of the text on post-it notes. Group these points into categories and place them at the bottom of a pyramid. Combine the grouped points into one point on the next level of the pyramid. Keep doing this until one point remains. Do this for both sides of the argument.

D After reading: Debate

Use the strategy of **Synthesising**. Use evidence from the text and your schema to debate the topic, 'Nuclear energy is not safe'.

Comprehension

 STOP! Use your dictionary to find out the meaning of the **bold** words below.

Nuclear Energy: Friend or Foe?

Nuclear energy is the **process** of producing energy through **fission**. At a nuclear power plant, **uranium atoms** are split in two, creating a great burst of heat energy. This process is carried out under water so that the water will boil and turn into steam. The steam turns a **turbine**, which powers a **generator**, which creates electricity. A similar process is carried out at other types of power plant, but by burning **fossil fuels** to heat the water.

Jakub

Good afternoon, Chairperson, **opposition** and ladies and gentlemen of the audience. I am here today to discuss nuclear energy. I hope to prove to you that the benefits of nuclear energy far **outweigh** the negatives. We all know that fossil fuels release carbon dioxide (or CO_2), which pollutes the environment and causes **climate change**. The main benefit of nuclear energy is that it **releases** only steam into the environment, not smoke. Steam does not contain CO_2 and is **consequently** not harmful to the environment. Therefore, nuclear energy is a clean source of energy. **Undoubtedly**, there are safety **concerns** with nuclear energy, just as there are with the creation of any type of energy. Indeed, more deaths and illnesses have been caused by coal mining than by nuclear power disasters. Nuclear power plants are much safer these days than they were in the past. They are now built with thick concrete walls. In addition to this, old plants have been shut down or updated and many plants are switching to **automated** systems, removing human error. This makes disasters very unlikely. Ladies and gentlemen, thank you for listening. I hope I have convinced you that nuclear energy is a clean, safe source of energy, making it a friend.

Good afternoon, Chairperson, **proposition** and ladies and gentlemen of the audience. I am here to prove to you that nuclear energy is, undoubtedly, a **foe**. Nuclear energy is simply not safe. We are all aware of the **tragic** explosion at Chernobyl, Ukraine in 1986, which released huge amounts of **radiation** into the local environment, sadly killing 53 people and poisoning many others. **Radioactive** material is unpredictable and unsafe. I'm sure you would all agree that we should not rely on such a **volatile** material for our energy needs. Secondly, the uranium used in a nuclear reactor produces highly radioactive waste, which remains toxic for thousands of years. There is no way to **dispose** of this waste, so it is stored in **sealed** barrels underground. Imagine if a natural disaster such as a flood, an earthquake or a landslide were to cause this radioactive waste to be released into the local environment, polluting water supplies. I'm sure you can agree that the damage would be **catastrophic**. Ladies and gentlemen, thank you for your attention. I am confident that I have convinced you nuclear energy is unsafe and, as a result, a foe.

Kelly

A **In your copy, go investigate.**

1. What is released into the environment when fossil fuels are burned?

2. How are nuclear power plants safer these days?

3. In what year did the Chernobyl disaster take place?

4. What is produced during the process of creating nuclear energy?

5. How is radioactive waste stored?

6. Explain the process by which nuclear energy is created.

B **In your copy, give your opinion.**

1. What is Kelly's opinion of nuclear energy? How do you know?

2. What energy source do you think would be better than nuclear energy? Why?

3. Do you think that nuclear waste is stored safely? Explain your answer.

4. Which side of the argument do you agree with? Why?

5. Would you like a nuclear power plant to be built near you? Why/Why not?

6. At the end of a debate, the proposition and opposition often ask each other questions about their speeches. Write two questions to ask each speaker.

C **Vocabulary: Match these cause-and-effect sentences.**

1. Uranium atoms are split in two. ■	■ It must be stored carefully.
2. The water boils and turns into steam. ■	■ Nuclear power plants are safer.
3. Burning fossil fuels releases CO_2. ■	■ The turbines turn.
4. The walls are made of thick concrete. ■	■ The environment is polluted.
5. Nuclear energy produces toxic waste. ■	■ Energy is created.

D **Cloze procedure: 'More About Energy'. Fill in the blanks.**

Fossil fuels are sources of _____ that come from decomposed plants and animals that were buried in the ground millions of years _____. Examples of fossil fuels include oil, natural gas, coal and peat or turf. Burning fossil fuels harms the _____ by releasing carbon _____ into the air. Fossil fuels are non-renewable, as they cannot be used _____. Nuclear energy is also non-renewable, as there is only a certain _____ of uranium in the world, but there is enough _____ to last for hundreds of years. Renewable energy is energy that can be used over and _____ again, e.g. solar energy, wind energy and hydro energy. These are clean sources of energy, as they _____ little to no carbon dioxide. However, these sources don't provide very much energy, whereas nuclear energy _____ a lot of energy with very little effort.

Phonics – 'ous' and '-ious'

'-**ous**' and '-**ious**' are suffixes added to a noun or a verb to make an adjective.

'-**ous**' is pronounced /**us**/, e.g. danger → danger**ous**.

'-**ious**' can be pronounced /**ee-us**/ or /**us**/, e.g. mystery → myster**ious** or relig**ious**.

A Complete these words using '-ous' or '-ious'.

| cur | enorm | jeal | delic | hazard |
| feroc | contag | ridic | fur | adventur |

B Change each noun or verb to an adjective using '-ous' or '-ious'.

1. fable   fabulous
2. vary
3. space
4. continue
5. suspicion
6. vigour
7. fame
8. grace
9. poison
10. religion

C Choose the correct word to complete each sentence.

disastrous   anonymous   famous   generous   anxious   vicious   obnoxious   spacious

1. "There is a _____ living room," the estate agent assured us.
2. My neighbour's dog is _____. It tried to bite me last week.
3. Each vote in an election must be _____.
4. Our school tour was _____. It rained all day!
5. Georgina's cousin is _____. He shouts in her ear and teases her constantly.
6. "Thank you for your gift. You're very _____," said Igor to his aunt.
7. Helen felt _____ before performing in the school musical.
8. "I would hate to be _____," said Eva. "I'd have no privacy."

Grammar – Sentences

A **clause** is a group of words that makes part of a sentence or a whole sentence.
A clause must have a verb, a subject and usually an object.
<u>Subject</u>: the noun or pronoun that performs the action
(Verb): the action being performed
Object : the noun or pronoun that receives the verb
Examples: <u>The dog</u> (ran) around the park .

A Underline the <u>subject</u>, ring the (verb) and box the object in these.

1. I went for a walk in the forest yesterday.
2. Kumar crashed his car this morning.
3. Our teacher loves to teach art.
4. The woman lost her purse.
5. Earth orbits the sun.
6. The librarian shushed the two boys.

A **sentence** is a group of words that makes complete sense. A <u>simple sentence</u> contains one clause, e.g. He watched TV. His sister did her homework.

A <u>compound sentence</u> contains two <u>simple sentences</u> joined by a **conjunction**, e.g. He watched TV **while** his sister did her homework.

B Tick 'simple' or 'compound' for each sentence.

	Simple	Compound
1.		
2.		
3.		
4.		
5.		
6.		

1. I snuck around the room, as my brother was sleeping.
2. The security guard stopped the robbery.
3. We named our goldfish Gogsy, because it has big eyes.
4. Janice packed her bag.
5. Niamh bought new football boots.
6. I won the race, even though I stumbled at the start.

C In your copy, join each pair of simple sentences to make one compound sentence.

1. Cillian eats his vegetables. They are good for him.
2. I saw a deer yesterday. I was out for a walk in the park.
3. Bernadette cut her arm badly. She went to the doctor.

D Dictation: Listen to your teacher and write the sentences in your copy.

I can do this!   I'm getting there.   I need help!

Oral Language

A Argument circle

As a class, sit in a circle. Start with the eldest pupil and move to the right. Each pupil must present a short argument 'for' the topic. Once everyone has spoken, move to the left and present an argument 'against'. Use the topics below or think of your own.

- All fossil fuels should be replaced with renewable sources of energy.
- Mobile phones should be banned from school.
- Pupils over the age of eleven should have two hours of homework.

Writing Genre – Persuasive Writing

The purpose of **persuasive writing** is to present a logical argument from a particular point of view. It may be written in the form of a debate, a letter or an advertisement.

Structure:
- **Statement** – States the problem or argument. This is sometimes presented as a question.
- **Argument** – Makes points arguing the position taken. The arguments 'for' are stated first, followed by the arguments 'against'.
- **Conclusion or summary** – A summary of the main points or position or an evaluation of the topic if no position was originally taken.

A Plan, organise and write a letter to a local councillor persuading them to invest government resources in renewable energy.

Wind energy		Solar energy		Hydropower		Biomass	

1. Plan your persuasive letter using some of the points listed below. Present a balanced argument by including some negatives.
   - Which renewable resource would you recommend? Why?
   - Benefits for the environment
   - Effect of fossil fuels on the environment
   - Money – cost and savings
   - Anything else that you can think of

2. Use the information in your plan to write the first draft of your persuasive letter. Each argument should be presented in a different paragraph in the form of:
   - Point
   - Elaboration
   - Evidence

B Drama: Stakeholders

Assign one of these roles to everyone in the class: scientist, electricity-company owner, farmer, local child, oil-company owner. Each of these roles is a stakeholder, i.e. someone who might be affected by the use of nuclear energy. In stakeholder groups, discuss your opinion of nuclear energy. Then, make new groups with one of each type of stakeholder in every group. Discuss your opinions with the group.

Which Tour?

Comprehension Strategies

A Before reading: Picture flick

Use the strategies of **Predicting** and **Questioning**. Look at the images next to the text. Make three predictions and write three questions that you have.

B During reading: Check your predictions and questions.

Were you right? Have any of your questions been answered?

C During reading: Fabulous five

Use the strategy of **Determining Importance**. While reading, record five key words in the text. Then, in groups, compare your 'fabulous five' and justify why you thought these were the most important words in the text.

activities   children   history   Tour   adventure

D After reading: Fact or fib?

Use the strategy of **Synthesising**. Write three facts and one fib about the text. Then, in pairs, swap your lists and find each other's fib.

Facts

1. _____

_____

2. _____

_____

3. _____

_____

4. _____

_____

Comprehension

STOP! Use your dictionary to find out the meaning of the **bold** words below.

Which Tour?

ART ATTACK!

Let your creativity flow in our specialised art village with three different activities chosen by you! Choose from:

- Clay creations
- Animal crafts
- Paint **prodigies**
- Tie-dye T-shirts
- Jewellery masters
- Monster truck **construction**

Price per child: €8

(Additional €1 per child for tie-dye T-shirts)

Teachers go free and are **provided** with tea or coffee.

Wow mums and dads with your creations!

NATURAL HISTORY MUSEUM

Explore the forgotten world of dinosaurs, woolly mammoths, the great Irish **elk** and much, much more.

Tour includes:

- Full guided tour with **fascinating insights** from our trained guides
- Historical **scavenger** hunt
- Free healthy snack

*Price per child: €2   Price per adult: €1

*Special **discount**: Take a guided tour of the National Art Gallery on the same day and pay only €1 each.

STEPPING STONES ADVENTURE CENTRE

Visit Ireland's highest-rated school tour destination.

Day Trips	Overnight Trips
Choose three activities.	Choose five activities.
Price per child: €25	Price per child: €100
Price per adult: €3	One teacher goes free for every 15 children.
	Lunch, dinner and breakfast are provided.

Note: All children should wear old, comfortable clothing and bring a change of clothes.

Choose from these action-packed activities:

Zip-lining
Nature walk
Canoeing
Water polo
Rock climbing

Spooky nighttime walk (overnight guests only)
Team-building (highly recommended)
Archery (strictly over 11s)
Orienteering
Paintballing (€1 extra per child)

A In your copy, go investigate.

1. How many activities can you do if you visit Art Attack?

2. Which tour involves a historical scavenger hunt?

3. How much would it cost for your class to attend Art Attack if you chose animal crafts, clay creations and tie-dye T-shirts?

4. Which tour provides free lunch, dinner and breakfast?

5. Name five activities that you could do at Stepping Stones Adventure Centre.

6. Would you be able to take part in archery? Why/Why not?

B In your copy, give your opinion.

1. Which tour would you like to visit? Why?

2. Which tour do you think your teacher would choose? Why?

3. What things might a teacher need to think about when booking a school tour?

4. Two of the activities cost extra. Why do you think this is so?

5. Might the design of the leaflets influence your decision? Explain.

6. What persuasive language can you see in the leaflets?

C Tick 'fact' or 'opinion' for each statement.

	Fact	Opinion

1. The Natural History Museum tour costs €2 per child.

2. You have to be good at art to attend Art Attack.

3. The Natural History Museum is a fascinating tour.

4. Art Attack provides tea and coffee for the teachers.

5. Stepping Stones Adventure Centre is the best tour.

6. The Natural History Museum provides a healthy snack.

D Cloze procedure: 'School Tour Disaster'. Fill in the blanks.

It was the last week of _____ and 5th Class were on their school tour at the Stepping Stones _____ Centre. They finished rock _____ and headed to the archery station. Luckily, everyone was over _____ years old. When the instructor finished _____ what they had to do, she walked up and down the line correcting their grip on the _____. Kevin and Heather were _____ to be sharing, but Heather wouldn't let _____ have a go. "Give it here!" shouted Kevin, tugging her arm as she let _____ of the arrow. It soared through the _____, caught the instructor's hat by the rim and pinned it to the ground. "We should have done the _____-building activities," their teacher sighed.

Phonics – '-tious'

'**-tious**' is a suffix added to a word to make an adjective. Usually, the root word ends in '**-tion**'. The suffix '**-tious**' is pronounced /**shus**/, e.g. nutri**tion** → nutri**tious**.

A Change each word to an adjective using '-tious'.

1. vexation _____vexatious_____
2. caution _____cautious_____
3. ambition _____
4. infection _____
5. superstition _____
6. nutrition _____
7. contention _____
8. pretension _____
9. repetition _____
10. fiction _____

B Complete the crossword using the '-tious' words above.

Down

1. Causing annoyance
2. Healthy to eat
3. To be very careful
5. Causing or involving an argument

Across

4. Not real, imaginary
6. To assume undeserved importance in oneself
7. Irrational fear of or belief in what is unknown or mysterious
8. Characteristic of a disease passed from one person to another
9. To do something over and over again
10. To wish to achieve success, power or wealth

C In your copy, write a short story using as many of the '-tious' words above as you can.

Grammar – Parts of Speech

An **article** is a word used to describe whether a specific or a general noun is being referred to. '**The**' is a **definite article**. It describes specific nouns, e.g. Close **the** door, please. '**A**', '**or**' and '**an**' are **indefinite articles**. They describe general nouns, e.g. I would like **a** drink.

A Insert the correct definite or indefinite articles in these. Then, ring the definite articles and box the indefinite articles.

1. Can I have _____ book for my birthday? I've read all of _____ books I own twice.

2. There is _____ elephant in _____ zoo named Upali.

3. _____ ambulance and _____ Gardaí were called to _____ scene of _____ crime.

4. Amanda had never been on _____ boat before _____ school trip last year.

5. Could you please tell me where _____ train station is?

An **interjection** is a word that shows emotion or feeling. It is often followed by a punctuation mark – usually an exclamation mark, e.g. Hey! Phew! Ouch!

B Match each interjection to the correct meaning or usage.

1. Boo!	▪ The sound of someone clearing their throat
2. Ahh!	▪ An expression of relief
3. Humph!	▪ Used to scare someone
4. Phew!	▪ Used to show you are fed up or disgruntled
5. Ahem!	▪ An expression of relaxation or satisfaction

There are nine main **parts of speech**: "<u>Ouch!</u>" (interjection) <u>said</u> (verb) <u>**Una**</u> (noun) <u>**as**</u> (conjunction) <u>she</u> (pronoun) <u>**tumbled**</u> (verb) <u>quickly</u> (adverb) <u>**down**</u> (preposition) <u>the</u> (article) <u>**steep**</u> (adjective) <u>**hill**</u> (noun).

C Colour the words to show parts of speech using the colours above. Look back over the grammar pages of this book to help you.

1. The tall girl ran quickly around the racing track.

2. "Yikes!" cried Gary when he found a huge spider in his shoe.

3. Ciarán sang beautifully at the concert, because he had practised.

4. Yolanda read her book yesterday, while she waited for the bus.

D Dictation: Listen to your teacher and write the sentences in your copy.

I can do this!   I'm getting there.   I need help!

Oral Language

A Trip to Mars

In groups of six, you are candidates for beginning a new civilisation on Mars. Assign one of these jobs to each person in the group:

- Doctor
- Farmer
- Garda
- Chef
- Teacher
- Scientist

Only four of you can be chosen to go. Explain to the group why your job makes you useful and why you should be chosen. Once everyone has presented their argument, discuss who should go and vote as a group.

Writing Genre – Persuasive Writing

The **language of persuasive writing** should include:

- nouns and pronouns that refer to general subjects, e.g. the government, nuclear fission.
- technical terms, e.g. atoms, contamination.
- usually timeless present tense, e.g. releases, costs. This can change if referring to the past or making predictions.
- formal objective styles, i.e. no personal pronouns. Personal opinions are presented as fact, e.g. everyone is aware that our planet is at risk.
- connectives that show cause and effect or problem and solution, that compare and contrast and show conclusion, e.g. as a result, however, therefore.

A Review, edit and rewrite your persuasive letter.

1. Make sure that your persuasive letter has all of the following:
   - Statement (position taken)
   - A conclusion
   - Arguments
   - Persuasive language

2. Read over your persuasive letter and edit it for spelling, punctuation and grammar.

3. Rewrite your persuasive letter and check that you have:
   - presented a logical and persuasive argument.
   - written it in the correct formal letter style.

4. Check your work using the persuasive self-assessment checklist.

Top tip!

Look back over Unit 6 to help you write your letter.

John Ryan,
123 The Rise,
Ballymun,
Dublin 9
12/5/18

Cllr Alma Glynn,
Ballymun Civic Offices,
Dublin 9

Dear Madam,

B Art activity

Create a poster to advertise one of the products or services listed below. Include pictures and text and use a lot of persuasive language.

- A breakfast cereal
- A health-food restaurant
- A car
- A mobile phone

18/12/18

Revision: Grammar and Phonics

Look back at the grammar on pages 53, 59, 65, 71, 77, 83, 89, 95 and 101.

Day 1

1. Tick for the underlined word.

   (a) Tania's book was <u>beneath</u> her bed.

   Adjective   Preposition ✓

   (b) I have two <u>older</u> brothers.

   Adjective ✓   Conjunction

   (c) I like exercise, <u>provided</u> it's indoors.

   Preposition   Conjunction ✓

2. Write as a contraction.

   (a) can not _can't_

   (b) it is _it's_

   (c) I would _I'd_

   (d) I am _I'm_

3. Add the correct punctuation.

   (a) Where are you going asked Laura?

   (b) "Don't worry," said Max "I can help."

4. Finish the tense table.

Past	Present	Future
drank	drink	will drink
felt	feel	will feel

5. Ring the correct spelling.

   (a) verssion / (version)

   (b) (percussion) / percusion

6. Change to an '-ation' noun.

   (a) celebrate _celebration_

   (b) investigate _investigation_

7. Change to an '-ify' verb.

   (a) class _classify_

   (b) identity _identify_

Day 2

1. Tick for the underlined word.

   (a) The cat ran <u>through</u> the park.

   Adjective   Preposition ✓

   (b) I study <u>in order to</u> do well in my tests.

   Preposition   Conjunction ✓

   (c) Joan took off her <u>worn</u> coat.

   Adjective ✓   Conjunction

2. Write as a contraction.

   (a) could have _could've_

   (b) I have _I've_

   (c) it will _it'll_

   (d) she had _she'd_

3. Add the correct punctuation.

   (a) Roger McGough wrote The Sound Collector.

   (b) "Today," announced Anna "is my birthday."

4. Finish the tense table.

Past	Present	Future
drove	drive	will drive
sat	sit	will sit

5. Ring the correct spelling.

   (a) (collision) / collission

   (b) (aggression) / aggresion

6. Change to an '-ation' noun.

   (a) converse _conversation_

   (b) associate _association_

7. Correct the spelling.

   (a) breakthroo _breakthrough_

   (b) althoa _although_

Revision: Grammar and Phonics

Day 3

1. Martha plays guitar.
   (a) Verb: _plays_
   (b) Subject: _Martha_
   (c) Object: _guitar_

2. Finish the adjective table.

Positive	Comparative	Superlative
big	bigger	_biggest_
clumsy	_clumsier_	_clumsiest_

3. Yesterday was Monday.
   Simple ✓   Compound

4. I like your coat, because it's blue.
   Simple   Compound ✓

5. Insert 'a', 'an' or 'the'.
   (a) May I have _an_ ice-cream?
   (b) I went to _the_ zoo.
   (c) I have _a_ younger sister.

6. Write the homonym: _right_
   (a) Opposite to left
   (b) Opposite to wrong

7. Match the rhyming words.
   (a) plant   kite
   (b) shed   aunt
   (c) height   bread

8. Finish the words with '-ous' or '-ious'.
   (a) enorm_ous_   (b) contag_ious_

9. Change to adjectives with '-ious'.
   (a) nutrition _nutritious_
   (a) caution _cautious_

10. Correct the spelling.
    (a) coff: _cough_
    (b) drowt: _drought_

Day 4

1. Insert an apostrophe.
   (a) had'nt   (b) Carlos's book
   (c) Sam's bag   (d) you're

2. Danny asked if he could borrow my book.
   Direct speech ✗   Indirect speech ✓

3. "Ouch!" exclaimed Mary. "That hurt."
   Direct speech ✓   Indirect speech ✗

4. Change these nouns to adjectives.
   (a) Ireland _Irish_
   (b) beauty _beatiful_
   (c) strength _strong_

5. She walked quickly to the park.
   (a) Noun: _park_
   (b) Verb: _walked_
   (c) Pronoun: _She_
   (d) Adverb: _quickly_

6. Write the homonym: _ring_
   (a) Jewellery worn on the finger
   (b) To call on the telephone

7. Match the rhyming words.

(a) stuff	eight
(b) plate	rough

8. Finish the words with '-ous' or '-ious'.
   (a) obnox_ious_   (b) ambidextr_ous_

9. Change to adjectives with '-ious'.
   (a) ambition _abitionious_
   (b) repetition _repetitionious_

10. Make '-sion' or '-ssion' nouns.
    (a) To permit: _permission_
    (b) To tense: _tension_

Assessment: Phonics

A Ring the correct spelling.

1. There was heavy traffic, because there had been a **collision** / **collission**.
2. The food in that restaurant is **delicous** / **delicious**.
3. Beef can become **tuff** / **tough** if it is cooked for too long.
4. 'Pull up your socks' is an **expression** / **expresion** that I don't understand.
5. Angela wrote an **anonymious** / **anonymous** poem for the school newspaper.
6. Many years ago, people **thought** / **thawt** that the earth was flat.

B Write the correct homonym.

1. The opposite of the truth
   To be horizontal on a bed or the ground

2. To run quickly in a competition
   A group related by country of origin

3. A migratory bird
   To consume food

4. A water-dwelling bird
   To get out of the way

5. The bottom of a shoe or foot
   A European flat fish

C Change these words to make nouns, verbs or adjectives by adding 'ation', 'ify' or 'tious'.

Noun		Verb		Adjective	
create		simple		nutrition	
hibernate		sign		infection	
decorate		justice		caution	

D Match the rhyming words.

1. said ▪   ▪ rough
2. power ▪   ▪ flower
3. loose ▪   ▪ sigh
4. stuff ▪   ▪ head
5. buy ▪   ▪ goose

6. fall ▪   ▪ window
7. pool ▪   ▪ eight
8. throw ▪   ▪ crawl
9. plate ▪   ▪ hum
10. come ▪   ▪ mule

Assessment: Comprehension

Sadko the Minstrel – a Traditional Russian Tale

Many years ago, in the city of Novgorod, there lived a minstrel named Sadko. He sang and played the goosli, an instrument like a harp that was laid across the knees, but he earned very little money.

One night, Sadko, who had not had a paying job for quite some time and was very hungry, sat by Lake Ilmen playing his goosli and singing softly to himself. Suddenly, he heard a beautiful voice singing back to him and glimpsed a young woman in the water. It was the Princess Volkova, whose father was the Tsar of the Sea.

"Play me another song," she called.

Sadko played and she danced on the water. When he was finished, she said, "Thank you for that beautiful music." She took three gold coins from her pocket and scattered them in the water. "Return quickly and cast your nets. You will catch three fish with fins of gold, which will bring you great wealth."

Sadko hurried home to retrieve his nets. However, along the way, he met a local merchant, who asked him to play at his feast. Sadko could not turn down an offer of real gold and so decided to return for the fish later.

Sadko played to a great hall full of rich merchants, who filled his cap with gold. As the banquet was coming to an end, the merchants began to boast. One boasted of his strength, another of his wealth and yet another of his skill in battle. Sadko, seeing an opportunity, got to his feet and called out, "I may not be strong, wealthy or skilled in battle, but I alone can catch fish with fins of gold."

The hall erupted with laughter. "It's true," Sadko assured them. "If you follow me to the banks of Lake Ilmen, I can show you." The merchants were so amused by this that they bet shops, ships or handfuls or gold, feeling sure that there could be no such thing in the lake.

Sadko seized a silken net and, with the city's richest merchants following in his wake, headed to the banks of Lake Ilmen. There he cast the net into the water. When he pulled the net out, there lay within three large fish with fins of gold.

The merchants could not believe their eyes, but they each honoured their word and gave Sadko the goods they had promised him. Sadko became the richest man in Novgorod and lived out his days playing music for pleasure and not for payment.

A In your copy, go investigate.

1. What type of instrument did Sadko play?

2. Why was Sadko hungry?

3. Why did Princess Volkova reward Sadko?

4. Did the merchants believe Sadko's story at first? How do you know?

5. How did Sadko become the richest man in Novgorod?

6. Do you think this is a true story? Explain.

6

B Ring the synonym and underline the antonym.

1. fragile: (weak)   heavy   sturdy   large
2. glance: whistle   stare   break   (glimpse)
3. similar: shining   (alike)   shimmer   different
4. foe: deer   friend   sister   (enemy)
5. fascinating: repair   boring   (interesting) clever

10

C Match each word with its meaning.

catastrophe	commotion	vanished	discount

1. Special reduced price   discount
3. Loud disturbance   commotion

2. Disastrous event   Catastophe
4. Disappeared   vanished

4

D Cloze procedure: 'The Birthday Party'. Fill in the blanks.

Dagmara had a party for her birthday. Her family decorated the house with purple and blue ballons and hung up a banner that said 'Happy Birthday, Dagmara !' All of her friends came and they played pin the tail on the donkey and had a water fight, as the weather was nice. Marta gave Dagmara a pink T-shirt with a flower on it. Róisín gave her some bracelets. But best of all was the present her best friend, Zainab, gave her; a big set of colouring pencils. Dagmara loved to draw and there were 30 colours for her to experiment with. Once the games were over and Dagmara had opened all of her presents, they had a sleepover. They laid out their sleeping bags in the sitting room, watched films, painted their nails and stayed up all night chatting. It was Dagmara's best birthday yet.

13

Assessment: Grammar

A In each of the sentences below:

Punctuation

1. Insert the correct punctuation.

2. Find an adjective, a preposition and a conjunction.

11

(a) Our grumpy teacher said "you can sit beside your friends as long as youre well behaved."

(b) "Have you seen Eamons new bag" asked Sara as she searched under the bed.

(c) I always keep *Skulduggery Pleasant* in my bag because its my favourite book.

Adjective	Preposition	Conjunction

9

B For each of the sentences below:

1. Tick 'simple' or 'compound'.

2. Ring the subject.

3. Underline the object.

Simple	Compound

9

(a) Mike hurt his leg, so he can't play football.

(b) She walked to the shop.

(a) I like dogs, because they are friendly

C Ring the mistake/s in each sentence.

1. Dog's are from the canine family, whereas bares are from the ursine family.

2. "I saw a elephant at the zoo" said Carl

3. Seáns brother is the fast boy in our hole school.

4. "Ouch?" exclaimed the angry man when someone stanted on his toe.

5. "Hey!" shouted Fabio. "You couldve hurt someone driving like that."

12

D Write these words as contractions.

1. she had ___she'd___   2. I would ___I'd___   3. it is ___it's___

4. will not ___wouldn't___   5. they are ___they're___   6. do not ___don't___

6

E Dictation: Listen to your teacher and write the sentences in your copy.

| I can do this! 👍 ⚪ | I'm getting there. 👎 ⚪ | I need help! 👎 ⚪ |

Dictation

Red indicates phonics covered in the unit.

Green indicates grammar.

Purple indicates an additional activity or a question revising grammar taught recently.

Unit 1: Capital letters, punctuation and homophones

1. I will celebrate my birthday next week. It's on the 18th of September.
2. "Ouch! I stepped on a piece of glass over there," said Tim.
3. Did you hear that 'Toy Story' will be on TV tonight?

- Write a homophone for as many words as you can.

Unit 2: Nouns and suffixes

1. We have a beautiful queen and a friendly king who rule our country wonderfully.
2. My brother is an excellent swimmer. We get great enjoyment from watching him race.
3. It gives me great happiness that my aunt and cousin are coming to my birthday party tomorrow.

- Underline the nouns in these sentences. Classify them as common or proper and then feminine, masculine, common or neuter.

Unit 3: Verbs, and '-age' and '-ege'

1. "It has been a privilege," said Mrs Lynch as she waved goodbye to her guest.
2. The sewage spillage on my street meant that I could not return home yesterday.
3. Shauna didn't bring much baggage when she went away to college.

- Underline the verbs. Don't forget the helping verbs.
- Ring the nouns.

Unit 4: Adverbs, and '-ible' and '-able'

1. The irresponsible boy ran quickly across the road when it wasn't safe.
2. I bought a refillable water bottle, so that I would not need to buy a new one daily.
3. "Ugh, this horrible sandwich is inedible!" cried Laura loudly as she ate her affordable lunch outside.

- Ring the adverbs in these sentences and sort them into adverbs of time, manner or place.

Unit 5: Commas and negative prefixes

1. "I thought dragons were non-existent," whispered Ned in disbelief.
2. Daniel's mother was incredulous when she heard he was misbehaving, irresponsible and disrespectful in school.
3. "The anti-theft devices on my tablet, mobile phone and laptop have malfunctioned," explained Mr Jones.

- Ring the nouns and underline the verbs in these sentences.

Unit 6: Pronouns and silent letters

1. <u>We</u> knitted <u>ourselves</u> new jumpers to wear in autum<u>n</u>.

2. <u>She</u> woul<u>d</u> not let her brother use the s<u>c</u>issors, as <u>they</u> were <u>hers</u>.

3. <u>They</u> asked the plum<u>b</u>er if <u>he</u> woul<u>d</u> like a bisc<u>u</u>it and <u>he</u> took <u>several</u>.

- Ring the silent letters in these sentences.

- Underline the pronouns. Remember that possessive adjectives are not pronouns. Can you find any in these sentences?

Unit 7: Singular/plural and '-tion'

1. The <u>children</u> agreed with the sugges<u>tion</u> that they should eat less sugar to prevent infec<u>tion</u> in their <u>teeth</u>.

2. The witch<u>es</u> said an incanta<u>tion</u> as they added fl<u>ies</u> and leav<u>es</u> to <u>their</u> po<u>tion</u>.

3. "Can I make a substitu<u>tion</u> of tomat<u>oes</u> instead of anchov<u>ies</u> on the pizza<u>s</u>?" asked Mary

- Change all of the plural nouns to singular nouns in these sentences.

- Underline the verbs in these sentences; can you change them to another verb that means something similar?

Unit 8: Assessment

1. "I think they're all dancing beautifully," said the solemn judge at the competition.

2. It's impractical to carry the biggest boxes if you're the smallest person.

3. Did she eat her salmon, butter and bread quickly before she went to college?

- Make a list of the nouns, verbs, adverbs and pronouns in these sentences.

Unit 9: Adjectives and '-sion'

1. My <u>enthusiastic</u> aunt loves any occa<u>sion</u> to have a <u>huge</u> celebra<u>tion</u>.

2. The <u>lazy</u> boy didn't finish the reading comprehen<u>sion</u>, but the <u>lazier</u> boy didn't even begin.

3. The <u>useless</u> builder made his <u>clumsiest</u> mistake when he miscalculated the dimen<u>sion</u>s of the exten<u>sion</u>.

- Can you change some of the '-sion' words to their root noun?

- Find the comparative and superlative adjectives.

- Can you think of any other adjectives you could use instead of these?

Unit 10: Speech marks and '-ssion'

1. <u>"</u>I love having discu<u>ssion</u>s about my obse<u>ssion</u> with Disney films<u>!"</u> exclaimed Ann.

2. <u>'</u>Harry Potter and the Goblet of Fire<u>'</u> was the fourth book written by profe<u>ssion</u>al author J. K. Rowling.

3. <u>"</u>I have a question about the submi<u>ssion</u> of our project<u>,"</u> said Bobby to his teacher<u>.</u> <u>"</u>Do I have permi<u>ssion</u> to type it<u>?"</u>

- Change sentence 1 to indirect speech.

- Can you write the root verbs of the '-ssion' words?

Unit 11: The apostrophe and '-ation'

1. "I**'ll** use Amy**'s** illustr**ation** as inspir**ation** for the decor**ation** on this cake!" cried Susan**'s** mum.

2. Hank**'s** parents keep getting lost on vac**ation**, because they**'re** finding the transl**ation** of the transport**ation** guide difficult to understand.

3. "You **can't** keep having convers**ation**s in class, because you**'re** damaging your educ**ation**," explained Aoife**'s** teacher.

▪ Rewrite the contractions as two words, e.g. we're – we are.
▪ Ring the proper nouns.
▪ Rewrite questions 1 and 2 as indirect speech.

Unit 12: Prepositions and '-ify'

1. The water **inside** that bucket will solid**ify** if it's left outside **through** the winter.

2. "Could you please ident**ify** the people **near** the bank **in** this photograph?" asked the Garda.

3. It is the scientist's job to class**ify** the samples **into** different groups and not to fals**ify** any results.

▪ Underline the prepositions in these sentences.
▪ Ring the nouns to which these propositions relate.

Unit 13: Verb tenses and '-ough'

1. Every day, the farmer **lays** down his pl**ough** and **gazes** thoughtfully at the birds as they **soar** thr**ough** the sky.

2. "I **brought** you some soup to help you **cure** that c**ough**!" **announced** Evan as he **burst** thr**ough** the door.

3. My mum **will help** me **to knead** the d**ough** thor**ough**ly, because it **will be** too t**ough** for me.

▪ Underline the verbs and identify the tense in these sentences.
▪ Can you change each sentence to another tense?
▪ Can you add adverbs before some of the verbs to make the sentences more interesting?

Unit 14: Conjunctions and homonyms

1. Hilda was forced to **duck** **as** the **swallow** flew overhead, **so** that it wouldn't hit her.

2. "I won a **ring** in the quiz, **because** all of my answers were **right**!" exclaimed Joanne **while** she walked home from school.

3. **Although** the **sole** of his shoe was wearing away, Nathan still won the **race**.

▪ Underline the conjunctions in these sentences.
▪ Write the definition of each homonym used in these sentences.
▪ Ring the pronouns.

Unit 15: Idioms and proverbs, and rhyming words

1. "<u>Two wrongs don't make a</u> _____!" cried David as he ran out of <u>sight</u>.

2. "<u>Pull up your</u> _____ and go catch that <u>fox</u>," said the farmer to his son.

3. I'm feeling a bit <u>under the</u> _____ since we went swimming <u>together</u>.

- Complete the idioms and proverbs in these sentences.
- Ring the two rhyming words.
- Rewrite question 2 as indirect speech.

Unit 16: Sentences, and '-ous' and '-ious' words

1. I (am) <u>jealous</u> of my |sister|, because <u>she</u> (is) more <u>adventurous</u> than I (am). **(c)**

2. The <u>ferocious</u> new |animal| in the zoo (is) very <u>dangerous</u>. **(s)**

3. I (contracted) a <u>contagious</u> |disease| while I (investigated) the <u>mysterious</u> new <u>poisonous</u> |plant|. **(c)**

- Label each sentence as simple or compound.
- Underline the subjects, ring the verbs and box the objects in these sentences.

Unit 17: Parts of speech and '-tious'

1. "<u>Oh!</u>" cried Orla. "You are <u>a</u> <u>pretentious</u> and <u>vexatious</u> person."

2. My mother told me <u>a</u> <u>fictitious</u> story about <u>an</u> <u>ambitious</u> giraffe.

3. "<u>Phew!</u>" said Harry when <u>the</u> doctor told him that his chicken pox were no longer <u>contagious</u>.

- Find a noun, a verb, an adjective, a pronoun, an interjection and a definite or indefinite article in each sentence.

Unit 18: Assessment

1. "Mum," said Paul, "can I have permission to go to Jack's enormous party?"

2. I brought some delicious and nutritious soup across the road to my new neighbour when he was feeling ill.

3. "Hey! You almost caused a collision," said the obnoxious man to Andy, even though he was being very cautious.

- Make a list of adjectives, prepositions and conjunctions in these sentences.

Cloze Procedure Answers

Unit 5

1. time	2. three	3. their
4. bricks	5. wolf	6. the
7. blow	8. onto (not up)	9. fire
10. ran		

Unit 6

1. Jane	2. dress/clothes/outfit	3. Mauve
4. too/as well	5. frilly	6. would
7. shoes	8. older	9. into/wearing
10. Aunty		

Unit 7

1. born	2. Renoir/he/Pierre	3. art
4. with	5. money	6. his
7. movement	8. they	9. time
10. death	11. works/pieces	12. artists/painters

Unit 8

1. Christmas	2. controlled	3. so
4. nails	5. she	6. centre
7. what	8. Andrew	9. Dad
10. their		

Unit 9

1. author	2. Potter	3. her/only/just
4. written	5. Joanne/Rowling/her	6. Harry
7. novel/book/story	8. much	9. won
10. them		

Unit 10

1. time	2. was	3. who
4. feet	5. Warden	6. is
7. Camp	8. did	9. his
10. lizards		

Unit 11

1. Buddhism	2. years	3. wanted/tried/wished
4. and	5. sign	6. travelled/roamed
7. One	8. he/Siddartha	9. suffering 10. known

Unit 12

1. an	2. computer	3. out
4. changed	5. computers	6. two
7. make/produce	8. and/or	9. days 10. world

Unit 13

1. who	2. escape/flee	3. family
4. the	5. Kitty	6. time/lives/experiences
7. time	8. discovered/found	9. she 10. diary

Unit 14

1. than	2. part	3. rising
4. acted/worked	5. one	6. She/Elizabeth
7. the	8. Pearse	9. taken 10. died

Unit 15

1. believe	2. at	3. job
4. air	5. live	6. grey
7. sounds/noises	8. ticking	9. windowpane
10. baby	11. thief/robber/collector	12. information/news
13. break/weather/ads		

Unit 16

1. energy	2. ago	3. environment
4. dioxide	5. again/twice	6. amount
7. left	8. over	9. release/produce/make
10. provides/gives/produces/makes		

Unit 17

1. school	2. Adventure	3. climbing
4. eleven	5. explaining	6. bow
7. supposed/meant	8. Kevin/him	9. go
10. air	11. team	

Unit 18

1. balloons	2. Dagmara	3. her
4. donkey	5. weather	6. star
7. friend	8. thirty	9. were
10. presents	11. bags	12. stayed
13. birthday		